Aiming for an ultra-sound Physics grade?

You've come to the right place — this CGP Exam Practice Workbook
will help push your marks towards the top end of the spectrum!

It's packed with challenging Grade 8-9 exam-style questions, sorted by topic
and perfectly matched to the latest AQA GCSE Physics course. What's more,
there are two sections of mixed practice to test you on a wider range of skills.

We've even included step-by-step answers at the back, so it's easy to check
your work and find out how to pick up any marks you missed out on.

CGP — still the best! ☺

Our sole aim here at CGP is to produce the highest quality books —
carefully written, immaculately presented and dangerously close to being funny.

Then we work our socks off to get them out to you
— at the cheapest possible prices.

Published by CGP

Editors:
Sarah Armstrong, Emily Garrett, Duncan Lindsay, Hannah Taylor, Stephen Walters and Charlotte Whiteley.

Contributors:
James Allen, Stuart Burditt and Ian Connor.

With thanks to Mark Edwards and Karen Wells for the proofreading.

With thanks to Ana Pungartnik for the copyright research.

ISBN: 978 1 78294 885 8

Data used to construct stopping distance diagram on page 40 from the Highway Code. Contains public sector information licensed under the Open Government Licence v3.0. http://www.nationalarchives.gov.uk/doc/open-government-licence/version/3/

Clipart from Corel®
Printed by Elanders Ltd, Newcastle upon Tyne

Based on the classic CGP style created by Richard Parsons.

Contents

✓ Use the tick boxes to check off the topics you've completed.

Topic 1 — Energy

Energy Transfers..1 ☐
Specific Heat Capacity, Power and Efficiency..2 ☐
Energy Resources...6 ☐

Topic 2 — Electricity

Circuits..7 ☐
Electrical Appliances and the National Grid..10 ☐
Static Electricity..13 ☐

Topic 3 — Particle Model of Matter

Density...14 ☐
Internal Energy and Changes of State..15 ☐
Particle Motion in Gases..18 ☐

Topic 4 — Atomic Structure

The Atomic Model and Nuclear Radiation..20 ☐

Mixed Questions for Paper 1

Mixed Questions for Paper 1...24 ☐

Topic 5 — Forces

Forces and Work Done..29 ☐
Pressure...33 ☐
Motion...35 ☐
More on Motion..37 ☐
Stopping Distances and Momentum...40 ☐

Topic 6 — Waves

Waves and Wave Behaviour..43 ☐
Electromagnetic Waves and Lenses..44 ☐
Radiation and Temperature...47 ☐
Exploring Structures Using Waves..48 ☐

Topic 7 — Magnetism and Electromagnetism

Magnetism and Electromagnetism..50 ☐
The Generator Effect and Transformers..52 ☐

Topic 8 — Space Physics

Red-Shift and Orbits...55 ☐

Mixed Questions for Paper 2

Mixed Questions for Paper 2...58 ☐

Answers..63
Equations List..80

Exam Tips

Exam Basics

1) For AQA GCSE Physics, you'll sit <u>two exam papers</u> at the <u>end</u> of your course.
   Each exam will last <u>1 hour 45 minutes</u> and each paper will be worth <u>100 marks</u>.

2) <u>Paper 1</u> tests you on <u>Topics 1-4</u> and <u>Paper 2</u> tests you on <u>Topics 5-8</u>.
   However, you're expected to know the <u>basic concepts</u> of physics in both papers.

Be Prepared to be Tested on Your Maths and Practical Skills

1) At least <u>30% of the total marks</u> for AQA GCSE Physics come from questions that test your <u>maths skills</u>.
   The maths questions won't always be straightforward. For example, for some of the harder maths questions
   you might need to interpret some <u>tricky data</u> or do a <u>multi-step</u> calculation. If you're aiming for a top grade
   you need to make sure you're comfortable with all the maths skills you've used in your course.

2) Around <u>15% of the total marks</u> will be from questions testing <u>practical skills</u>. For example, you might be asked
   to comment on the <u>design</u> of an experiment (the <u>apparatus</u> and <u>methods</u>), make <u>predictions</u>, and <u>analyse</u> or
   <u>interpret results</u>. You'll be tested on some of the <u>required practical activities</u> you'll have done as part of your
   course, but you'll also be expected to <u>apply</u> your practical knowledge to <u>unfamiliar experiments</u> — acing these
   questions will really show the examiners you know your stuff.

Here are a Few Handy Hints

1) **Always, always, always make sure you <u>read the question properly</u>.**
   This is a simple tip but it's really important. When you've got so much knowledge swimming
   round in your head it can be tempting to jump right in and start scribbling your answer down.
   But take time to make <u>absolutely sure</u> you're answering the question you've been asked.

2) **Take your <u>time</u> with <u>unfamiliar contexts</u>.**
   Examiners like to test you really understand what you've learnt by asking you to apply your knowledge in
   <u>different ways</u>. Some of these contexts can be quite tricky but don't let them trip you up — read all the
   information you're given <u>really carefully</u> and, if you don't understand it, <u>read it again</u>. You can make notes
   alongside the question or underline certain bits if it helps you to focus on the <u>important</u> information.

3) **Look at the <u>number of marks</u> a question is worth.**
   The number of marks gives you a pretty good clue as to <u>how much</u> to write. So if a question is worth four
   marks, make sure you write four decent points. And there's no point writing an essay for a question that's
   only worth one mark — it's just a waste of your time.

4) **Write your answers as <u>clearly</u> and <u>accurately</u> as you can.**
   For some open response questions, as well as being marked on the scientific content of your answer,
   you'll also be marked on the <u>overall quality</u> of it. So always make sure your answers have a <u>clear
   and logical structure</u>, you include detailed, <u>relevant</u> information and you answer the question <u>fully</u>.

5) **Show <u>each step</u> in your <u>calculations</u>.**
   You might be a bit of a whizz at maths and be confident that your final answer to a question will be right,
   but everyone makes mistakes — especially when under the pressure of an exam. Always write things out
   in <u>steps</u>. Then, even if your final answer's wrong, you'll probably pick up <u>some marks</u> for your method.

6) **Pay attention to the <u>time</u>.**
   After all those hours of revision it would be a shame to miss out on marks
   because you didn't have <u>time</u> to even attempt some of the questions.
   If you find that you're really struggling with a question, just <u>leave it</u>
   and <u>move on</u> to the next one. You can always <u>go back to it</u> at the
   end if you've got enough time.

These handy hints might help you pick up as many marks as you can in the exams — but they're no use if you haven't learnt the stuff in the first place. So make sure you revise well and do as many practice questions as you can.

Energy Transfers

1 A catapult uses stretched elastic to fire objects at speed. A stone is fired horizontally into a box that is hanging from the ceiling. The stone is caught in the box and the box swings upwards, as shown in **Figure 1**.

Figure 1

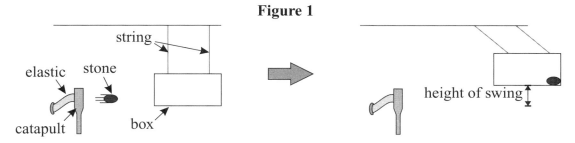

After the stone lands in the box, the swing reaches a maximum height of 20 cm.
The stone has a mass of 20 g and the box has a mass of 100 g.
The gravitational field strength is 9.8 N/kg.

1.1 Calculate the speed of the stone just before it hit the box. You may assume that all the energy in the kinetic energy store of the stone was transferred to the gravitational potential energy stores of the stone and the box. Give your answer to two significant figures.

Speed = ... m/s

[6]

To fire the stone, the elastic was pulled so that its total length was twice its original length.
The stone is fired again. This time the elastic is pulled so that it is four times its original length.
It can be assumed that the elastic in the catapult is never stretched past its limit of proportionality.

1.2 What effect does this have on the energy transferred to the kinetic energy store of the stone?
Tick **one** box.

The energy transferred is two times larger than the first time. ☐

The energy transferred is three times larger than the first time. ☐

The energy transferred is four times larger than the first time. ☐

The energy transferred is nine times larger than the first time. ☐

[1]

[Total 7 marks]

Score: ☐

7

 ☐   ☐   ☐

Specific Heat Capacity, Power and Efficiency

1 A cool box is a highly insulated container used for keeping food and drinks at a low temperature.

A student does an experiment to test the quality of insulation of a cool box, using the equipment shown in **Figure 1**. The student uses ice packs to bring the temperature inside the cool box down to –10 °C. He then leaves the cool box in a hot room.

The student measures the temperature inside the cool box every 1000 s, using a temperature probe and data logger.

Figure 1

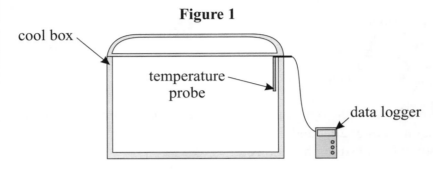

The student plots the results of his experiment on the graph shown in **Figure 2**.

Figure 2

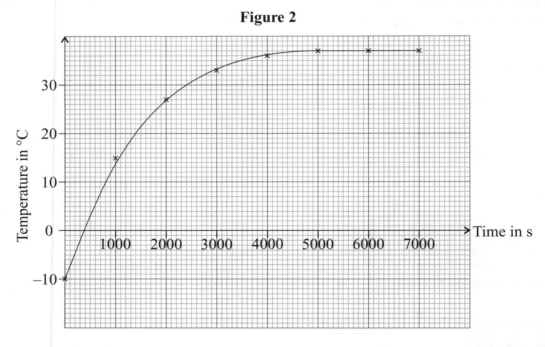

1.1 Using **Figure 2**, determine the instantaneous rate of temperature change inside the cool box 2000 s after the start of the experiment.

Rate of temperature change = ... °C/s

[3]

1.2 The walls of the cool box have a specific heat capacity of 1800 J/kg°C.
The cool box has a mass of 2.0 kg.
Calculate the instantaneous rate of energy transfer from the surroundings to the cool box 2000 s after the start of the experiment.

Rate of energy transfer = ... J/s

[2]

1.3 The freezer used to freeze the ice packs for the experiment has an efficiency of 95%.
The freezer has an input power of 250 W.
Calculate the useful energy transferred by the freezer in 20.0 minutes.

Energy transferred = ... J

[5]

[Total 10 marks]

2 A student is carrying out an experiment to determine the specific heat capacity of lead. She heats a 6 kg block of lead using the apparatus shown in **Figure 3**.

Figure 3

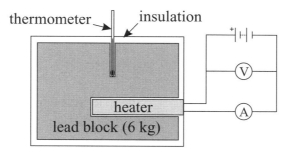

2.1 The circuit supplies 0.1 kW of useful power to the lead.
The student calculates that, during 9 minutes of use, the circuit wastes 300 J of energy to the thermal energy stores of the surroundings.
Calculate the efficiency of the circuit. Give your answer to two significant figures.

Efficiency = ...

[6]

The student plots the results of her experiment on a graph to show how the temperature of the lead changes with time, as shown in **Figure 4**.

Figure 4

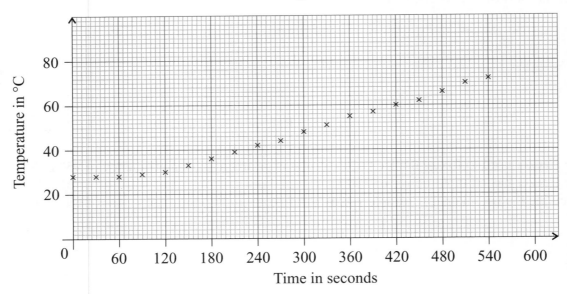

2.2 Using **Figure 4**, estimate what the temperature of the lead would be 10 minutes after the start of the experiment if she continued heating the lead block.

Temperature = ... °C

[2]

2.3 Calculate the specific heat capacity of lead, using **Figure 4**.
Give your answer to three significant figures.

Specific heat capacity = ... J/kg°C

[6]

2.4 Explain how the value obtained for the specific heat capacity would change if the insulation around the lead block had a higher thermal conductivity.

....

....

....

....

....

....

[3]

[Total 17 marks]

3   A solar panel is attached to an insulated tank that contains 3000 kg of liquid X, as shown in **Figure 5**. The solar panel absorbs energy from the Sun during the day and transfers some of that energy to liquid X.

Figure 5

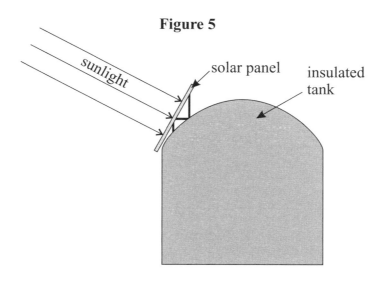

The useful energy that is transferred to liquid X in one day is 47.5 MJ.
This causes the temperature of liquid X to increase by 4.0 °C.

3.1 Calculate the specific heat capacity of liquid X.
Give your answer to three significant figures.

Specific heat capacity = ... J/kg°C

[4]

The solar panel is in sunlight for approximately 12 hours per day.
The average solar power that would be incident on the solar panel is 5 kW.

3.2 Estimate the efficiency of the panel.
Give your answer to two significant figures.

Efficiency = ...

[5]

[Total 9 marks]

Exam Practice Tip

In some high demand questions, you'll need to do multiple calculations before you get your final answer. It can be easy to make a mistake if you try to juggle all that information in your head. Write down all your working — it may get you marks even if you get the final answer wrong.

Score:

36

Topic 1 — Energy

Energy Resources

1   Britain's energy supply is mostly provided by coal-fuelled power stations, but the use
of other resources is increasing. One source of power that is being used more is wind power.

1.1* Evaluate the benefits and drawbacks of using more wind power
and less coal to supply Britain's energy needs.

....

....

....

....

....

....

....

....

....

....

[6]

The histogram in **Figure 1** shows the distribution of wind speeds at a wind turbine site
during one week.

Figure 1

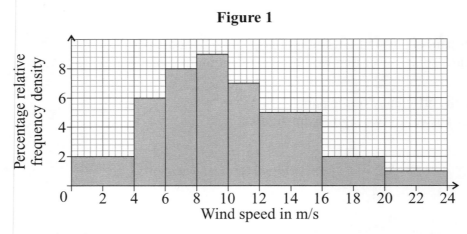

Wind speed in m/s

1.2 Calculate the percentage of time for which the wind speed was greater than 10 m/s.

Percentage time = ... %

[2]

[Total 8 marks]

Score:

8

Topic 1 — Energy

Circuits

1   A student has connected a circuit, shown in **Figure 1**. The circuit contains
     a 6.0 V cell, a thermistor, a 1.0 Ω resistor and two voltmeters, V_1 and V_2.

Figure 1

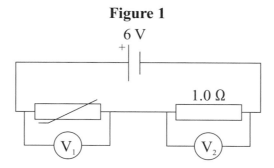

1.1   The current through the thermistor is 0.50 A. The voltmeter V_1 reads 5.5 V.
      The current consists of a flow of electrons and each electron carries a charge of 1.6×10^{-19} C.
      Calculate the number of electrons that will flow through the thermistor in 2.0 hours.

Number of electrons = ...
[3]

1.2   The circuit is moved to a different room, where the temperature is 16 °C.
      The reading on V_1 is now 0.25 V.
      Calculate the resistance of the thermistor when the external temperature is 16 °C.
      Give your answer to three significant figures.

Resistance = ... Ω
[6]

1.3   The student wants to connect a heater in parallel with one of the components, so that when the
      external temperature decreases, the potential difference across the heater increases and it gets hotter.
      Explain which component the heater should be connected across in order for this to work.

      ....

      ....

      ....

      ....

      ....
[3]
[Total 12 marks]

2   A student conducts an experiment to find how the length of a wire affects its resistance. The graph of her results is shown in **Figure 2**.

Figure 2

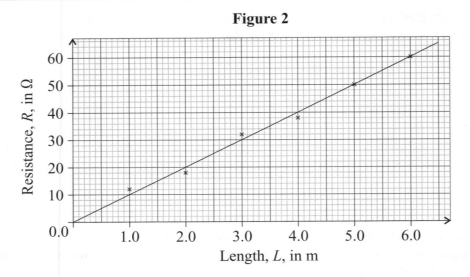

Length, L, in m

2.1 Determine the equation of the line of best fit in **Figure 2**, in terms of resistance, R, and length, L.

Equation: ....
[2]

2.2 A 0.375 m length of this wire is used in a circuit.
A potential difference of 0.5 kV is applied across the wire.
Calculate the current that flows through the wire. Give your answer to three significant figures.

Current = ... A
[5]

2.3 The resistance of a wire is inversely proportional to its cross-sectional area.
The wire the student used in her experiment has a cross-sectional area of 0.11 mm².
A second wire made from the same material has a cross sectional area of 0.44 mm².
By considering **Figure 2**, what would be the resistance of a 1.2 m length of this second wire?
Tick **one** box.

24 Ω ☐

12 Ω ☐

3 Ω ☐

48 Ω ☐

[1]
[Total 8 marks]

3 A student builds the circuit shown in **Figure 3**.

The resistor has a constant resistance of 1.6 Ω. The power supply initially supplies a potential difference of 1.0 V. At this point, the bulb has a resistance of 1.0 Ω.

Figure 3

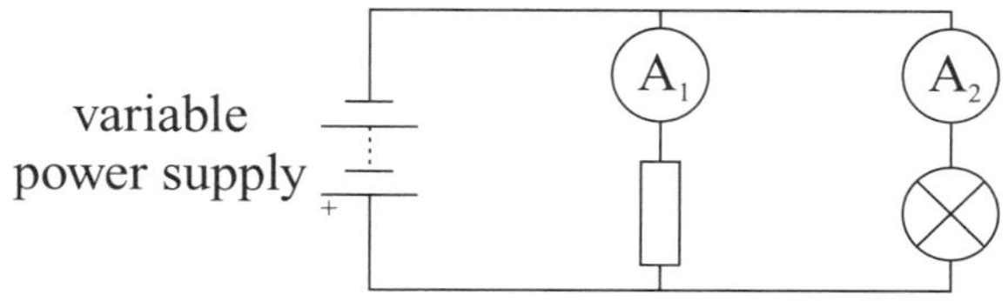

variable power supply

3.1* Explain how the reading on ammeter A_1 compares to the reading on ammeter A_2 as the potential difference of the power supply is increased.

....

....

....

....

....

....

....

....

....

....

[4]

The student creates a new circuit containing the variable power supply, the resistor and component X connected in series. The *I-V* characteristic of component X is shown in **Figure 4**.

Figure 4

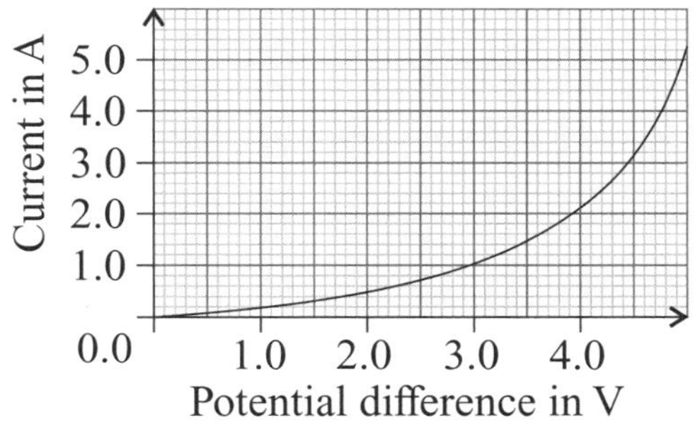

Current in A vs Potential difference in V

3.2 Using **Figure 4**, explain how the total resistance of the circuit changes as the potential difference of the power supply is increased.

....

....

....

....

....

....

[3]

[Total 7 marks]

Score:

26

Electrical Appliances and the National Grid

1   A rollercoaster uses an electric motor to push each car round an uneven section of track.

A joulemeter is connected to a data logger and used to monitor the energy transferred by the motor. **Figure 1** shows the graph produced by the data logger.

Figure 1

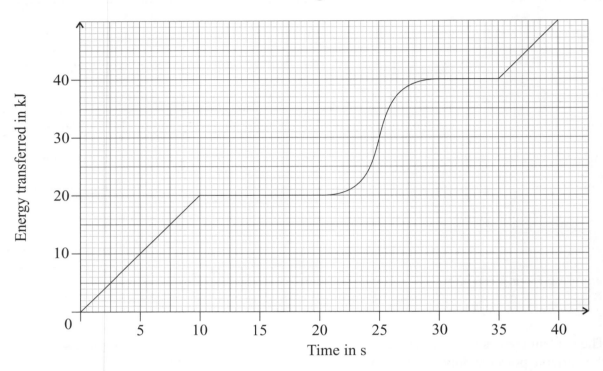

1.1   Using **Figure 1**, calculate the maximum instantaneous power supplied by the motor.
Give your answer to three significant figures.

Power = ... W
[4]

1.2   Between 20 s and 30 s, a total of 12 C of charge passes through the motor.
Using **Figure 1**, calculate the average potential difference across the motor during this time.
Give your answer to two significant figures.

Average potential difference = ... V
[5]

1.3 In the supply cable that connects the motor to the electricity supply, the average power wasted due to heating is 36 W. The resistance of the cable is 250 mΩ.
Calculate the average current through the cable.

Average current = ... A

[3]

1.4 The owner of the rollercoaster buys electricity in units. Each unit supplies 3.6×10^6 J of energy.
In a month, the supply cable wastes 7.56 units worth of energy due to heating.
Calculate the number of hours the rollercoaster is used for in a month.

Time = ... hours

[5]

[Total 17 marks]

2   Substations, such as the one shown in **Figure 2**, are a part of the national grid.
They contain a number of electrical devices, such as transformers, that are used
to adjust the mains electricity supply before it reaches consumers.

Figure 2

2.1 The electricity transferred to a transformer in the substation has a power of 1.843 GW.
Once passed through the transformer, the electricity has a current of 166 kA. The power of
the electricity coming out of the transformer is 99% of the power supplied to the transformer.
Calculate the potential difference of the electricity after it has passed through the transformer.
Give your answer to three significant figures.

Potential difference = ... V

[5]

One of the cables near the substation breaks and comes into direct contact with the metal body of a car, as shown in **Figure 3**.

Figure 3

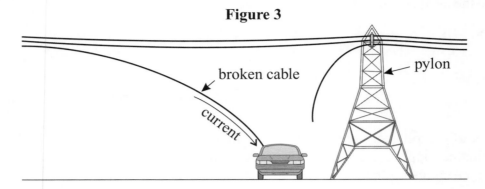

A current flows through the cable to the car for 0.55 s before the supply is cut off.
The cable transfers electricity with a power of 0.31 GW.

2.2 The potential difference between the cable and the car is 380 kV.
Calculate the total charge that is transferred to the car during the fault.
Give your answer to two significant figures.

Charge = ... C

[6]

2.3 Charge cannot flow through the car's tyres, so there is now a large potential difference between the car and the ground. Suggest why it would be dangerous for a person to approach the car.

....

....

....

....

....

....

[2]

[Total 13 marks]

Exam Practice Tip

Challenging exam questions will often present you with new and unfamiliar situations. You might not have met them on your course, but you will have learnt the physics you need to understand them. Read the question carefully, and look for similarities with examples you recognise.

Score: ☐ / **30**

Static Electricity

1   A student rubs together two insulating objects. When the student tries to move
them apart, he feels a force of attraction between the two objects. He finds that
the attractive force decreases as the objects are moved further apart.

1.1* Explain why there is an attractive force between the objects, and why the strength of the force
changes with distance. You should refer to electric fields in your answer.

....

....

....

....

....

....

....

....

....

....

[4]

The student has a gold leaf electroscope, shown in **Figure 1**.
The electroscope consists of a flask containing a metal disc
attached to a metal rod with two thin gold foil leaves at the end.

The student touches one of the insulating objects
to the metal disc. This causes the disc, rod and
gold leaves to become positively charged.
This causes the gold leaves to rise up.

Figure 1

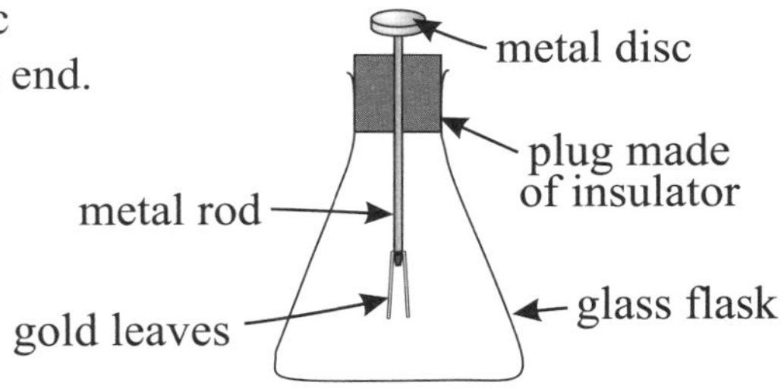

metal disc
plug made
of insulator
metal rod
glass flask
gold leaves

1.2 Which of the following diagrams shows the electric field around the gold leaves? Tick **one** box.

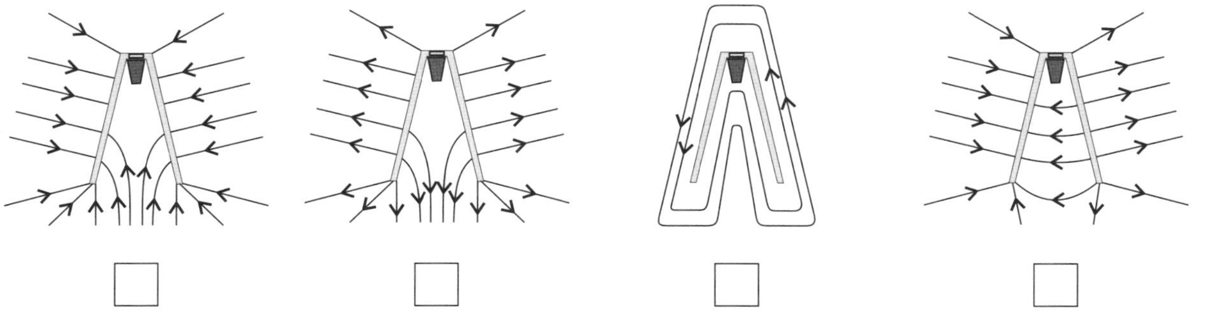

☐   ☐   ☐   ☐

[1]

[Total 5 marks]

Score: ☐

5

Density

1   Aerogels are man-made solids with an extremely low density.

A company produces an aerogel with a density of 1.50 kg/m³. **Figure 1** shows a block of the aerogel floating in some water. The aerogel has a mass of 0.50 kg. The volume of the aerogel below the waterline is 5×10^{-4} m³.

Figure 1

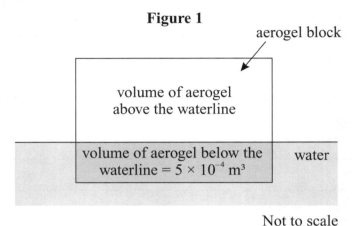

aerogel block

volume of aerogel above the waterline

volume of aerogel below the waterline = 5×10^{-4} m³

water

Not to scale

1.1   Calculate the percentage of the volume of the aerogel that is below the waterline.

Percentage = ... %

[4]

1.2   The company can make 0.360 m³ of the aerogel in 24 hours.
Calculate the average rate of production of the aerogel. Give your answer in grams per minute.

Rate of production = ... g/min

[5]

[Total 9 marks]

Exam Practice Tip

If you're not sure where to start with a problem, try checking the units given in the answer — sometimes they'll offer clues about how the answer is calculated. For example, if it's a mass unit over a volume unit, you'll probably need to divide a mass by a volume.

Score: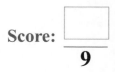

9

Internal Energy and Changes of State

1   Ball A is a 50 g ball made of aluminium. Ball A is heated and then
plunged into 1.0 kg of water that has an initial temperature of 27 °C.
The water and the ball eventually reach the same temperature of 30 °C.

1.1   Calculate the temperature of ball A just before it was plunged into the water.
Assume no energy is lost to the surroundings.
The specific heat capacity of water is 4200 J/kg°C.
The specific heat capacity of aluminium is 900 J/kg°C.

Temperature = ... °C

[5]

1.2   Ball A is removed from the water and then heated at a constant rate for 45 minutes.
Figure 1 shows the temperature-time graph for ball A as it is being heated.

Figure 1

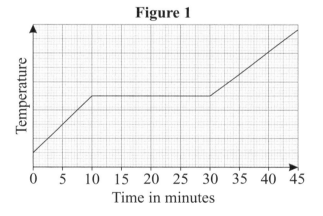

Time in minutes

Ball B is another aluminium ball. Ball B has half the mass of ball A.
On **Figure 1**, draw the temperature-time graph of ball B that would be produced
if energy was transferred to it at the same rate as ball A. Explain your answer.

....

....

....

....

....

....

[4]

[Total 9 marks]

Topic 3 — Particle Model of Matter

2   **Table 1** shows the specific heat capacities of different substances.

Table 1

Substance	Specific heat capacity in J/kg°C
Tin	217
Ammonia (liquid)	4700
Ammonia (gas)	2060

An electric heater is used to transfer energy to different substances. It is assumed that no energy is wasted to the surroundings and no energy is transferred from the surroundings to the substances.

2.1 The heater is used to transfer 740 J of energy to a piece of tin.
The temperature of the tin increases by 30 °C.
Calculate the mass of this piece of tin. Give your answer to two significant figures.

Mass = ... kg
[4]

2.2 The heater continues to heat the tin at a constant rate.
Once the tin reaches a certain temperature, the temperature of the tin stops changing.
Explain why.

....

....

....
[2]

2.3 The heater is then used to heat 30 g of ammonia. The ammonia is initially a liquid with a temperature of –60 °C. The ammonia boils at a temperature of –33 °C and then its temperature rises to –10 °C. The heater supplies a total of 46.3 kJ of energy to the ammonia during this time.

Calculate the specific latent heat of vaporisation of ammonia.
Give your answer to three significant figures.

Specific latent heat of vaporisation = ... J/kg
[6]

[Total 12 marks]

3   A chocolate manufacturer carries out an experiment to find the specific latent heat of fusion of their chocolate, which melts at 32 °C.

Figure 2

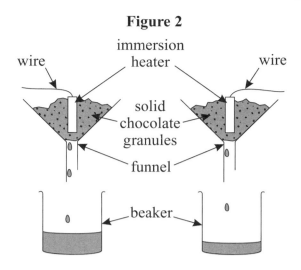

The experiment is carried out in a tropical cocoa plantation where the air temperature is 35 °C.

Figure 2 shows the two sets of equipment that are used. In each set, a funnel is placed above an empty beaker. Each funnel is filled with solid chocolate granules and then an immersion heater is placed inside. The immersion heaters are identical. The right-hand immersion heater is never switched on.

3.1   What is the purpose of the right-hand set of equipment? Tick **one** box.

It is used to detect anomalous results. ☐

It is used to find the specific heat capacity of the chocolate. ☐

It is used to find the mass of chocolate melted due to energy transferred from the surroundings. ☐

It is used to show that the experiment is reproducible. ☐

[1]

3.2   The left-hand immersion heater has a power of 60 W and is switched on for 90 seconds. Before the experiment, the masses of the beakers were measured. After the heater is switched off, the masses of the beakers and their contents are measured again. The results are shown in **Table 2**.

Table 2

Object	Mass in g	
	Left-hand equipment	Right-hand equipment
Beaker alone	70	70
Beaker and melted chocolate	210	90

Calculate the specific latent heat of fusion of the chocolate.
Assume that no energy is lost to the surroundings during the experiment and that the temperature of the chocolate in both funnels is 32 °C throughout the experiment.

Specific latent heat of fusion = ... J/kg
[5]

[Total 6 marks]

Score: ☐

27

 ☐   ☐   ☐

Topic 3 — Particle Model of Matter

Particle Motion in Gases

1   **Figure 1** is a graph that shows the relationship between depth underwater and pressure.

Figure 1

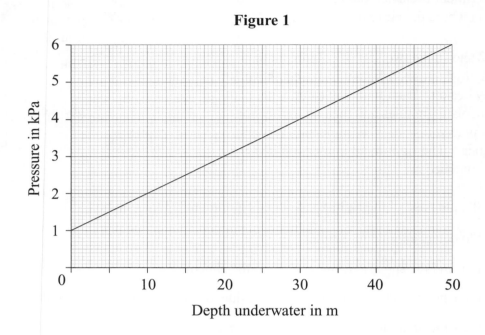

1.1 A diver notices that underwater air bubbles increase in size as they rise up.
Explain why this happens.

....

....

....

....

....
[2]

1.2 A bubble produced underwater at a depth of 25 m moves upwards. By the time the
bubble reaches 10 m below the surface, it has expanded to a volume of 1000 cm³.
Use **Figure 1** to calculate the volume of the bubble at a depth of 25 m.
Assume the bubble maintains a constant temperature as it travels upwards.
Give your answer to two significant figures.

Volume = ... cm³
[4]

[Total 6 marks]

2   **Figure 2** shows an oxygen cylinder. Oxygen cylinders are rigid metal containers in which oxygen is stored. They are sometimes used by climbers at the top of mountains.

Figure 2

2.1 Use your knowledge of the particle model to explain why the pressure inside an oxygen cylinder decreases as oxygen is removed from it.

....

....

....

....

....

....

[3]

2.2* A climber carries an oxygen cylinder up a mountain. The temperature decreases as the climber gets higher up the mountain. Explain how the pressure in the oxygen cylinder changes as it is carried up the mountain.

....

....

....

....

....

....

....

....

....

[4]

[Total 7 marks]

Score:

13

Topic 3 — Particle Model of Matter

Topic 4 — Atomic Structure

The Atomic Model and Nuclear Radiation

1   **Figure 1** shows part of the periodic table which includes the symbol, name and atomic number of different elements.

Figure 1

Symbol: Name: Atomic number:	K potassium 19	Ca calcium 20	Sc scandium 21	Ti titanium 22
Symbol: Name: Atomic number:	Rb rubidium 37	Sr strontium 38	Y yttrium 39	Zr zirconium 40
Symbol: Name: Atomic number:	Cs caesium 55	Ba barium 56	La lanthanum 57	Hf hafnium 72

1.1 Yttrium-93 can undergo radioactive decay to form zirconium-93.
State the type of radioactive decay that yttrium-93 undergoes.

....

[1]

1.2 Write a nuclear equation for this decay of yttrium-93.

....

[2]

1.3 Caesium-112 decays by emitting a single particle to form iodine-108.
Explain the changes in the caesium nucleus for this decay.

....

....

....

[2]

1.4 Using **Figure 1** and your answer to 1.3, calculate the atomic number of iodine.

Atomic number = ...

[1]

1.5 Titanium is formed by fusion in stars.
Which element could form titanium by fusion with another element? Tick **one** box.

Calcium   ☐   Strontium   ☐

Rubidium   ☐   Caesium   ☐

[1]

1.6 The part of the periodic table in **Figure 1** doesn't give a value for the mass number of each element. Suggest why this is not usually possible.

....

[1]

[Total 8 marks]

2 A village's water supply comes from a nearby lake. The lake has been contaminated with a nuclear material. The graph in **Figure 2** shows how the count-rate measured in the lake changes over time.

Figure 2

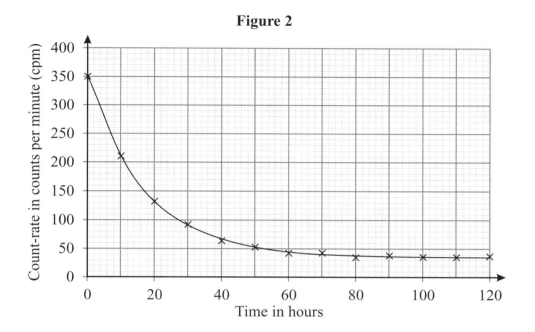

2.1 The count-rate measured was not corrected for background radiation.
Using **Figure 2**, estimate the background radiation count-rate.

Background radiation = ... cpm
[1]

2.2 Draw a line on **Figure 2** showing how the corrected count-rate changes over time.
[2]

2.3 Estimate the half-life of the sample.

Half-life = ... hours
[2]

2.4 The water is safe to drink when the corrected count-rate of the contaminated water falls below 25 counts per minute. The decay curve was produced using data from a radiation detector which is accurate to ± 5 cpm. How many hours after the source of contamination has stopped will the water first become safe to drink? Explain your answer.

....

....

....
[2]

2.5 The water company won't declare contaminated water safe to drink until it has been below 25 counts per minute for more than 24 hours. Suggest why this is the case.

....

....
[1]

[Total 8 marks]

3   **Figure 3** shows how radiation can be used to check for cracks in metal turbine blades in jet engines.

Figure 3

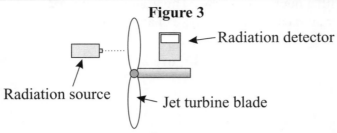

Radiation source

Radiation detector

Jet turbine blade

3.1 The blades are several centimetres thick. Suggest what type of radiation the source should emit.

....

[1]

3.2 Explain how the equipment in **Figure 3** could be used to detect a crack in a turbine blade.

....

....

....

....

[3]

[Total 4 marks]

4   Radioactive isotopes are used as tracers in medical imaging.

4.1 The radioactive isotope iodine-131 has a half-life of 8.0 days and an atomic number of 53.
It is used as a medical tracer. It is taken into the body and a detector outside the body traces its
position. Iodine-131 undergoes beta decay and then gamma decay to form stable xenon (Xe).
Write **two** nuclear decay equations to show these processes.

1. ....

2. ....

[4]

4.2 Give **two** reasons why iodine-131 is a suitable radioactive isotope to be used as a medical tracer.

1. ....

    ....

2. ....

    ....

[2]

4.3 Iodine-131 can be used in radioiodine therapy to treat thyroid cancer. Iodine-131 capsules are
taken by the patient and the isotope travels to the thyroid where it kills cancer cells with radiation.
Suggest why patients often have to stay in hospital and why there are strict limitations on visitors.

....

....

....

[2]

[Total 8 marks]

5   Uranium-235 is a radioactive material used as fuel in fission reactors. It releases both
     gamma rays and alpha particles as part of the decay process. Workers at nuclear power
     stations wear protective suits, as shown in **Figure 4**, when working with uranium-235.

Figure 4

Breathing mask
with filter

Sealed zips

Radiation shielding material
shields against alpha, beta
and some gamma radiation

Protective gloves

5.1* Evaluate the risks of contamination and irradiation from the different types of radiation emitted
     by uranium-235. Include an explanation of how the design of the protective suit in **Figure 4**
     protects the user from these risks.

     ....

     ....

     ....

     ....

     ....

     ....

     ....

     ....

     ....

     ....

     [6]

5.2 Uranium-235 undergoes nuclear fission in a nuclear reactor. Which decay equation shows the
     nuclear fission of uranium-235 in a nuclear chain reaction? Tick **one** box.

     $^{235}_{92}U + {}^{1}_{0}n \rightarrow {}^{92}_{36}Kr + {}^{144}_{56}Ba$ ☐

     $^{235}_{92}U \rightarrow {}^{92}_{36}Kr + {}^{141}_{56}Ba + 2{}^{1}_{0}n$ ☐

     $^{235}_{92}U + {}^{1}_{0}n \rightarrow {}^{92}_{36}Kr + {}^{141}_{56}Ba + 3{}^{1}_{0}n$ ☐

     [1]

     [Total 7 marks]

Exam Practice Tip

A lot of this section comes back to understanding the different types of decay. Once you know the
properties of alpha, beta and gamma decay you can apply that knowledge to all sorts of questions
about nuclear equations, irradiation, contamination, uses of radiation and so on.

Score:

35

 ☐   ☐   ☐

Topic 4 — Atomic Structure

Mixed Questions for Paper 1

1   When some stars explode, they leave behind a very dense object called a neutron star.

1.1   A neutron star has a mass of 2.1×10^{30} kg and a volume of 1.4×10^{13} m^3. A sugar cube has a volume of 1.0×10^{-6} m^3. Calculate how much mass a sugar cube with the same density as this neutron star would have.

Mass = ... kg

[5]

1.2   It is thought that the core of a neutron star consists of neutrons that are closely packed together. Explain, using the nuclear model of the atom, why solid matter found on Earth is much less dense than neutron star matter.

....

....

....

[2]

1.3   The Sun releases approximately 4×10^{26} J of energy per second. The kind of explosions that produce neutron stars can release as much as 1×10^{44} J of energy. Calculate how many years it would take for the Sun to release this amount of energy if it continued releasing energy at the same rate. Give your answer to one significant figure.

Time taken = ... years

[3]

1.4   Every star starts its life as a gas cloud. Explain how the pressure in the gas cloud changes if the cloud is heated by a nearby star, assuming the gas cloud has a constant volume.

....

....

....

....

[3]

[Total 13 marks]

2 A skyscraper has a total height of 300 m.

2.1 A lift inside the skyscraper carries tourists to the top. The lift has a mass of 1200 kg.
The maximum mass that the tourist lift can carry in addition to its own weight is 700 kg.
The energy the lift uses to travel the full 300 m to the top of the building at full capacity is 9310 kJ.
Calculate the efficiency of the lift at full capacity. The gravitational field strength is 9.8 N/kg.

Efficiency = ...

[4]

2.2 A service lift in the building has double the power of the tourist lift. The maximum mass of the
service lift and its contents is four times the maximum mass of the tourist lift and its contents.
Explain how the average speed of the service lift will compare to the tourist lift at full capacity.
Assume both lifts have the same efficiency.

....

....

....

....

....

[4]

2.3 The service lift is fitted with a 75 W light bulb. The potential difference
across the light bulb is 120 V. Calculate the resistance of the light bulb.

Resistance = ... Ω

[5]

2.4 A coin is dropped from the top of the building. It falls 300 m to the ground.
Calculate the speed of the coin just before it hits the ground.
State any assumptions you make. Give your answer to two significant figures.

Speed = ... m/s

[5]

[Total 18 marks]

3   **Figure 1** shows the International Space Station (ISS). The ISS is a spacecraft in orbit around the Earth that astronauts can live on. When decommissioned, it will have to be removed from space, probably in a controlled crash landing into the sea.

Figure 1

NASA/ESA/SCIENCE PHOTO LIBRARY

The ISS takes 90 minutes to complete one full orbit of the Earth.
For half of the orbit the ISS passes through the shadow of the Earth in complete darkness.
The ISS is powered by arrays of solar cells. Another option for powering a spacecraft is nuclear power. Nuclear generators have a lifetime longer than the expected lifetime of the ISS, whereas solar cells do not. Both power sources are capable of providing enough power for the ISS.

3.1* Evaluate the advantages and disadvantages, other than cost, of each method of powering the ISS.

....

....

....

....

....

....

....

....

....

....

[6]

3.2 Liquid ammonia is used as a coolant for the solar cells used to power the ISS. The ammonia is pumped around the solar cells in pipes and the solar cells transfer energy from their thermal energy stores to the thermal energy stores of the coolant. The specific heat capacity of ammonia is 4600 J/kg°C and the density is 680 kg/m³. Calculate the amount of energy needed to heat 0.5 m³ of ammonia by 5 °C. Give your answer to two significant figures.

Energy = ... J

[5]

3.3 A backup battery system is charged by the solar cells while they are exposed to the sunlight to supply energy while the ISS is in darkness.

The battery circuits have a total resistance of 0.96 Ω and the battery has a steady potential difference of 240 V across it while charging. Calculate the amount of charge transferred to the backup battery system as it is recharged when exposed to sunlight in each orbit of the Earth. Give the unit.

Charge = ... Unit = ...

[5]

Figure 2 shows data about the average background radiation doses measured in different locations. Radiation dose is measured in sieverts (Sv). A higher dose leads to an increased risk of developing cancer.

Figure 2

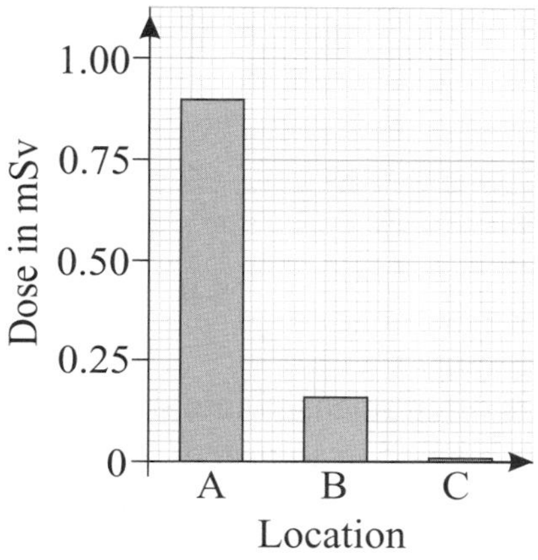

A - Average background radiation dose per day measured on board the ISS
B - Average background radiation dose per day measured on a plane in flight
C - Average background radiation dose per day measured in Cornwall

3.4 Suggest an explanation for the results shown in **Figure 2**.

....

....

....

....

....

....

[3]

3.5 Suggest why both astronauts and pilots have to wear devices that measure radiation dose at work.

....

....

....

[2]

[Total 21 marks]

4   **Figure 3** shows a boiling water nuclear reactor.

Figure 3

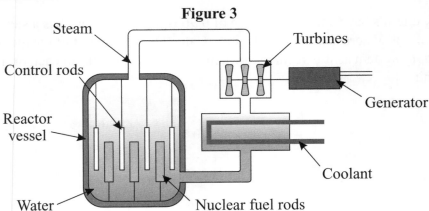

4.1 In a nuclear reactor, the nuclear fuel rods generate huge amounts of energy which heat the water surrounding the fuel rods. As the water is heated it boils and turns into steam. The steam rises and turns the turbines, generating electricity in the generator.
     Which of the following increases the energy produced by a nuclear reactor? Tick **one** box.

Cooling the steam before it reaches the turbines. ☐

Increasing the boiling point of the water in the reactor. ☐

Increasing the number of secondary fissions caused
by each fission in the chain reaction. ☐

Adding more neutron-absorbing control rods. ☐

[1]

4.2 A beta-emitting radioactive isotope called iodine-131 is often released into the air during nuclear accidents. It can settle on skin and clothing and can be inhaled or ingested. Iodine is absorbed in the body by the thyroid gland, where it is used to make molecules that travel throughout the body. When the thyroid gland has enough iodine, any excess iodine is removed by the body. If a nuclear accident occurs at a power plant, workers are asked to ingest potassium iodide tablets which contain a stable isotope of iodine. Explain how this minimises the risk of damage to their bodies.

....

....

....

....

....

....

[4]

[Total 5 marks]

Exam Practice Tip

Think carefully about the questions in this mixed topic — they might seem to be asking about one topic, but actually need information from another. You might need to draw together your knowledge from different areas of the course, so bear that in mind if you get stuck.

Score: ☐
──
57

Mixed Questions for Paper 1

 ☐   ☐   ☺ ☐

Forces and Work Done

1   A rocket is launched on a mission to land on the Moon.

Figure 1 shows the rocket at a particular point in time as it
moves directly upwards through the Earth's atmosphere.
The upwards force acting on the rocket from the engines is 40.0×10^6 N.
The rocket has a weight of 7.60×10^6 N.
The air resistance acting on the rocket is 9.40×10^6 N.

1.1 Draw **one** vector arrow from the × marked on **Figure 1** to represent the magnitude and direction
of the resultant force acting on the rocket. Use a scale of 1 mm = 10^6 N.

Figure 1

[2]

The Earth's gravitational field strength, g, varies with the distance from the Earth,
and can be calculated using the equation:

$$g = \frac{GM_E}{r^2}$$

where: r = the distance from the centre of the Earth in m
        M_E = the mass of the Earth in kg = 5.97×10^{24} kg
        G = gravitational constant = 6.67×10^{-11} N m²/kg²
The distance of the Moon from the centre of the Earth is 3.84×10^8 m.

1.2 The weight of the Moon due to the Earth's gravitational field is 1.98×10^{20} N.
Calculate the mass of the Moon. Give your answer to three significant figures.

Mass = ... kg
[6]

[Total 8 marks]

2   A child in a sled is being pulled up a slope by an adult, as shown in **Figure 2**.

Figure 2

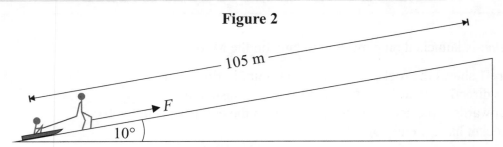

The adult applies a constant force, F, to the child and sled, parallel to the slope.
The adult does work on the sled and child to pull them 105 m along the slope. In doing work,
5.44 kJ of energy is transferred to the child and sled's gravitational potential energy stores.
The remaining 2270 J of work is done against resistive forces acting on the sled.

2.1 Calculate the size of the force F. Give your answer to three significant figures.

Force = ... N

[5]

2.2 The adult travels down the same slope shown in **Figure 2** on their own sled at a constant speed.
The friction acting on the sled parallel to the slope is 125 N.
The normal contact force acting on the adult and sled perpendicular to the slope is 710 N.
Draw a scale drawing on the grid below to calculate the combined weight of the adult and sled.

Weight = ... N

[3]

[Total 8 marks]

Topic 5 — Forces

3 An engineer is building a rope swing as part of an assault course. For safety reasons, when a person is on the swing, the rope must not extend by more than 7 cm.

The engineer is deciding between two ropes, A and B, to make the swing from.
The force-extension graphs for samples of the two ropes are shown in **Figure 3**.
The samples used were the correct length for use in the rope swing.
The elastic limit of each sample is labelled E.

Figure 3

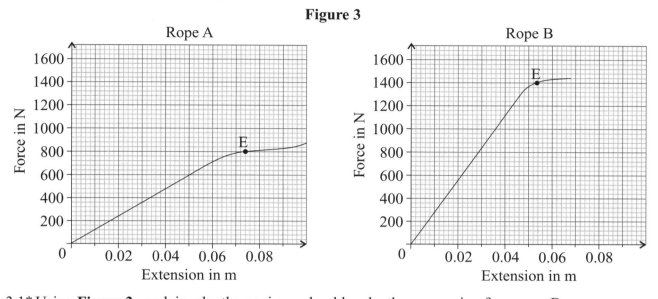

3.1* Using **Figure 3**, explain why the engineer should make the rope swing from rope B.
It can be assumed that the average weight of a person is 700 N.

....

....

....

....

....

....

....

....

[4]

3.2 Using **Figure 3**, calculate the extension of rope B when 21.0 J of work is done to stretch it from its original length. Give your answer to three significant figures.

Extension = ... m

[5]

[Total 9 marks]

4   A plank is in equilibrium and rests on two supports.

The plank is 6.0 m long, has a uniform density and a mass of 10 kg.
A mass of 10 kg is placed on the plank at point B, as shown in **Figure 4**.

There is a support at point A, at one end of the plank. Another support is positioned at point C.
The distance from A to C is twice the distance from C to the end of the plank, D.
Point B is halfway between the supports.

Figure 4

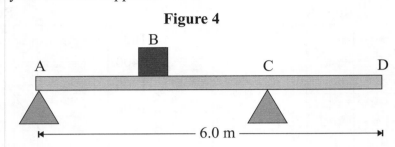

4.1   Calculate the upwards force acting on the plank at point A.
Gravitational field strength = 9.8 N/kg.

Force = ... N

[5]

Levers can be used to vary the force needed to lift a load.
The mass at point B can be raised in two different ways:

•   by pressing down at point D and pivoting about C, or,
•   by lifting up at D and pivoting about A.

4.2   Which of these methods requires a larger force to raise the mass by the same height?
Tick **one** box.

Pressing down on the plank at point D.   ☐

Lifting up the plank at point D.   ☐

It requires the same force to move the block by both methods.   ☐

[1]

[Total 6 marks]

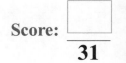

Exam Practice Tip

Some questions will involve a lot of variables and additional information. As you work through
the question, it may be helpful to add labels and notes to the diagrams you've been given.
This can help you keep track of extra information and calculations all in one place.

Score: ☐

31

Topic 5 — Forces

Pressure

1   An aeroplane is flying at an altitude (height) of 35 000 feet.

Explain why the aeroplane consumes less fuel while travelling at a given speed at 35 000 feet
than it does while travelling at the same speed at a lower altitude.
You should refer to the density of air in your answer.

....

....

....

....

....

[Total 3 marks]

2   A jug containing water has oil poured into it.
The oil collects on the surface of the water, as
shown in **Figure 1**. The layer of oil is 2 cm thick.

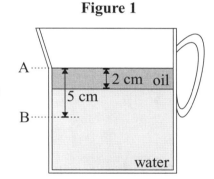

Figure 1

The difference in pressure between point A, at the surface of the
oil, and point B, 5 cm below the surface of the oil, is 470.4 Pa.
The density of water is 1000 kg/m³.

2.1   Calculate the density of the oil.
Gravitational field strength = 9.8 N/kg.

Density = ... kg/m³
[5]

2.2   Which of the following graphs correctly shows how the pressure changes with depth below the
surface of the oil? The dotted line shows the boundary between the oil and water.
Tick **one** box.

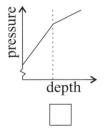   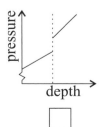   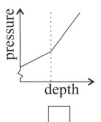   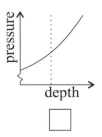

☐   ☐   ☐   ☐

[1]
[Total 6 marks]

3   The typical internal pressure due to compressed air in an aerosol can is 500 kPa.

3.1   Calculate the total force exerted on the inside walls of a typical aerosol can by the compressed air.
      Give your answer to three significant figures.
      Assume that a typical aerosol can is a perfect cylinder of height, $h = 20$ cm and radius, $r = 2.5$ cm.
      Surface area of a cylinder $= 2\pi r(r + h)$.

      Force = ... N

      [5]

The aerosol can is placed in a bucket of water and held at the bottom of the bucket,
as shown in **Figure 2**.

Figure 2

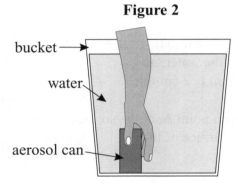

The average density of the aerosol can and its contents is 375 kg/m³.
The density of water is 1000 kg/m³.

3.2   Explain what happens when the can is released.
      You should refer to the forces acting on the can in your answer.

      ....

      ....

      ....

      ....

      ....

      ....

      ....

      ....

      [4]

      [Total 9 marks]

      Score:

      18

Topic 5 — Forces

Motion

1   An average speed camera calculates the average speed of a car by measuring
     the time it takes to travel between two sensors that are a set distance apart.

     A car is travelling down a road, and passes the first sensor of an average speed camera.
     Just after the car passes the first sensor, the car travels a distance of 740 m in 27 s. It then
     travels 1400 m in 50 s, and finally travels another 360 m before passing the second sensor.
     The average speed camera calculates the car's average speed between the sensors as 27.2 m/s.

1.1 Calculate the time it took for the car to travel the last 360 m.
     Give your answer to three significant figures.

                                                  Time = ... s
                                                                                            [4]

Figure 1 shows the distance-time graph of the first 300 s of the car's journey, before it reached
the speed camera.

Figure 1

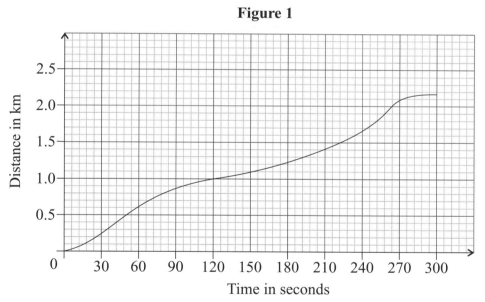

1.2 Calculate the maximum speed reached by the car during the first 300 s of the journey.
     Give your answer in km/h and to two significant figures.

                                                  Speed = ... km/h
                                                                                            [5]
                                                                           [Total 9 marks]

Topic 5 — Forces

2   A ferry is carrying passengers between two islands, as shown in **Figure 2**.

Figure 2

The velocity-time graph of the ferry during its journey is shown in **Figure 3**.

Figure 3

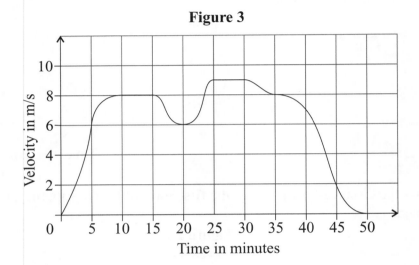

2.1 The speed of boats is often measured in knots. 1 knot ~ 0.5 m/s.
     Which of the following is the maximum speed reached by the ferry during its journey?
     Tick **one** box.

4.5 knots   ☐   18.0 knots   ☐

15.5 knots   ☐   4.0 knots   ☐

[1]

2.2 Using **Figure 3**, estimate the average speed of the ferry during its journey.

Average speed = ... m/s
[4]
[Total 5 marks]

Exam Practice Tip

Remember to pay close attention to the labels on graphs. You may be familiar with the quantities the graph is showing, but the units used and the scales of the axes can be more unusual. Make sure you take this into account when reading from the graph and making any calculations from it.

Score: ☐
14

More on Motion

1   A child is throwing stones directly down into a pond from a height of 0.75 m above the surface.
      It can be assumed that air resistance is negligible and the stone accelerates downwards at 9.8 m/s².

1.1   A stone is thrown with an initial speed of 1 m/s.
      Calculate the time taken for the stone to hit the surface of the water after being thrown.
      Give your answer to two significant figures.

                                                           Time = ... s
                                                                                                    [6]

Figure 1 shows the velocity-time graph of the stone from the point at which it is thrown.
The dotted line shows the point at which the stone entered the water.

Figure 1

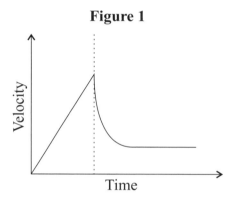

1.2* Using **Figure 1**, describe the forces acting on the stone as it falls through the air and water.
      Your answer should include a description of how the forces affect the stone's motion.

      ....

      ....

      ....

      ....

      ....

      ....

      ....

      ....

      ....

      ....
                                                                                                    [6]
                                                                                 [Total 12 marks]

2   A student is investigating how the force applied to a trolley affects its acceleration. They use the setup shown in **Figure 2**. The student changes the force on the trolley by altering the angle of the ramp.

Figure 2

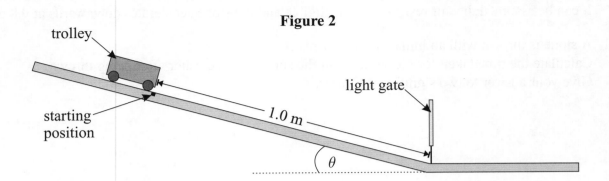

trolley
light gate
starting position
1.0 m
θ

The trolley is held at rest at the starting position. It is released and allowed to roll down the ramp.

The light gate measures the final velocity of the trolley at the bottom of the ramp.
The student uses this to calculate the acceleration down the ramp.
The student also calculates the resultant force acting on the trolley in the direction of its motion.

Figure 3 shows the graph of their results.

Figure 3

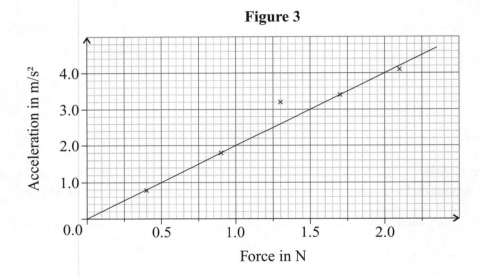

Acceleration in m/s²
Force in N

2.1 Using **Figure 3**, determine the inertial mass of the trolley.

Inertial mass = ... kg

[3]

When the resultant force was 1.3 N, the student recorded an anomalous result for acceleration.
This was because the trolley had a non-zero initial velocity.
At a force of 1.3 N, the light gate recorded a final velocity of 2.53 m/s.

2.2 Using **Figure 3**, calculate the initial velocity of the trolley for the anomalous result.
Give your answer to two significant figures.

Initial velocity = ... m/s

[5]

This experiment can be used to model the behaviour of a car as it rolls down a hill.
Assuming friction is negligible and the only force acting to move a car down a hill is its weight,
a car will accelerate down a hill with an incline of 10° at approximately 1.8 m/s².

2.3 Estimate the size of the braking force which must be applied in order for a car to remain at a
constant speed as it rolls down a hill with a 10° incline.

Force = ... N

[3]

[Total 11 marks]

3   A parachutist falling towards the Earth exerts an attractive force of 680 N on the Earth. Explain
the cause of this force and explain why the Earth does not noticeably move towards the person.

....

....

....

....

....

....

....

....

....

[Total 4 marks]

Score:

27

Topic 5 — Forces

Stopping Distances and Momentum

1 **Figure 1** shows two graphs that illustrate how the thinking distance and braking distance of a moving car vary with the speed of the car in good driving conditions.

Figure 1

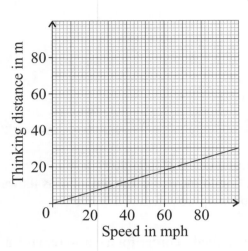 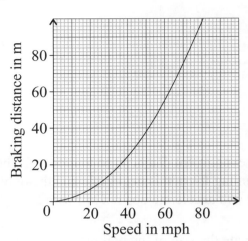

1.1* Explain the shapes of the graphs shown in **Figure 1**.
In your answer you should refer to relevant equations of motion and energy transfers.

....

....

....

....

....

....

....

....

....

....

....

[6]

1.2 Using **Figure 1**, estimate the stopping distance of a car when it is travelling at 33 m/s.
1 mph = 0.447 m/s.

Stopping distance = ... m

[3]

1.3 Explain how the two graphs in **Figure 1** would be different
for driving conditions where the road is slippery.

....

....

....

....

....

....

[4]

[Total 13 marks]

2 Two people are investigating each other's reactions times.

Person 1 measures the reaction time of Person 2 by dropping a ruler between their thumb and
index finger. Person 2 has to catch the ruler as soon as possible after noticing that it is falling.

Person 2's arm is resting on the table with their hand free to catch the ruler.
The 0.0 cm mark on the ruler is initially held level with Person 2's thumb.

2.1 Person 1 measures Person 2's reaction time to be 0.20 s.
Calculate the distance the ruler fell before Person 2 caught it.
Give your answer in centimetres. Acceleration due to gravity = 9.8 m/s^2.

Distance = ... cm

[5]

2.2 Suggest **two** changes that could be made to improve the experiment.
Explain your answers.

1. ....

....

....

2. ....

....

....

[4]

[Total 9 marks]

3 An engineer is testing a rifle. When the rifle is fired, the rifle 'jumps' backwards at the same time as firing the bullet. This is known as recoil.

3.1 Explain why it is not possible to fire the rifle without the rifle recoiling.

....

....

....
[2]

3.2 Suggest **one** change that could be made to a rifle to reduce its recoil velocity. Explain your answer.

....

....
[2]

3.3 A bullet with a mass of 10.0 g is fired to the right from a rifle with a mass of 4.00 kg. The rifle recoils with a velocity of 1.00 m/s to the left. The bullet strikes a stationary wooden block with a mass of 500 g and becomes lodged in it. Calculate the velocity of the wooden block directly after the bullet becomes lodged in it. Assume the speed of the bullet remains constant as it travels from the rifle to the block. Give your answer to three significant figures.

Velocity = ... m/s
[5]

3.4 When a person fires a rifle, they often hold the back of the rifle against their shoulder. Rifles can be fitted with deformable pads on the back as a safety feature. Explain how the deformable pads act as a safety feature.

....

....

....

....

....
[3]

[Total 12 marks]

Score:

34

Topic 5 — Forces

Investigating Wave Properties

1 A student sets up a ripple tank in a dark room.

Figure 1

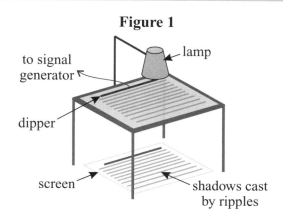

She puts a screen beneath the tank, then sets up a lamp above the tank. She attaches a signal generator to the dipper in the tank. When she turns the signal generator on, ripples are generated and their shadows can be seen on the screen below. The shadow lines are the same size as the waves. Her experimental set-up is shown in **Figure 1**.

1.1 The student finds that the total distance between the first and last of ten shadow lines is 27 cm. The waves have a period of 0.25 s.
Calculate the speed of the waves produced by the dipper.

Speed = ... m/s
[5]

1.2 Another student suggests moving the lamp to the side of the tank so that it shines down on it at an angle. Suggest why they should **not** do this.

....

....
[1]

1.3 The student replaces the lamp with a stroboscope but keeps the rest of the set-up the same.
A stroboscope flashes a bright light at regular time intervals.
The student adjusts the time interval of the flashes until the ripples appear to stop moving.
Give the time interval used by the student to achieve this effect. Explain your answer.

....

....

....

....
[2]
[Total 8 marks]

Score:

8

Electromagnetic Waves and Lenses

1   An object is placed on the left-hand side of a convex lens. The lens has a focal length of 40 mm.

1.1   A 26 mm tall image is formed to the left of the lens, 60 mm from the lens. Complete **Figure 1** by constructing an accurate ray diagram showing the size and location of the object. The lens, the axis of the lens, the principal focus points and the image have been drawn for you.

Figure 1

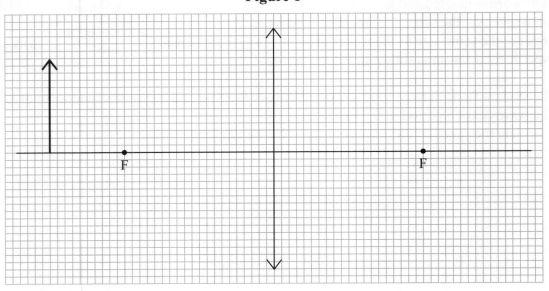

[4]

1.2   The object is moved so that it is 80 mm from the lens. Which option describes the image produced by the lens? Tick **one** box.

The image is real and upright. ☐

The image is real and upside down. ☐

The image is virtual and upright. ☐

The image is virtual and upside down. ☐

[1]

1.3   The equation below can be used to calculate the magnification of a lens.

$$\text{magnification} = \frac{\text{image distance}}{\text{object distance}}$$

A new object is placed at a distance of 0.16 m from the lens, which produces an image at a distance of 0.40 m from the lens. The image is 12 cm tall. Calculate the height of the object.

Height = ... cm

[5]

[Total 10 marks]

2   A paint manufacturer has to ensure that each new batch of paint is the same as the other batches of the same colour of paint.

Figure 2

One way of checking this is by using a spectrophotometer on a sample of the paint, as shown in **Figure 2**. Spectrophotometers can record the percentage of light reflected by a sample across a range of wavelengths.

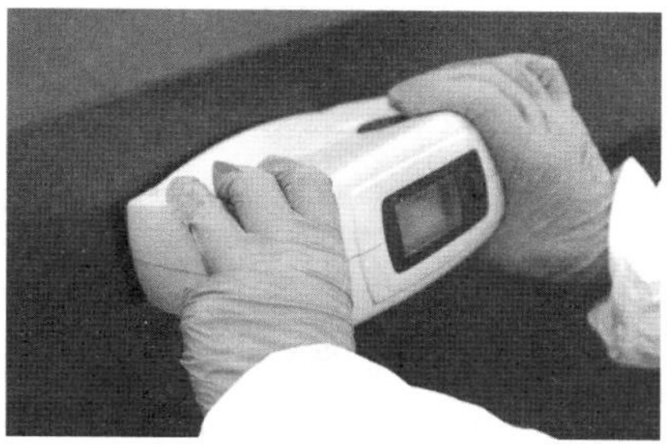

Table 1 shows the frequencies of different colours of visible light. The spectrophotometer display for a particular paint is shown in **Figure 3**.

Table 1

Colour	Frequency in THz
Violet	750
Indigo	670
Blue	640
Green	570
Yellow	520
Orange	500
Red	450

Figure 3

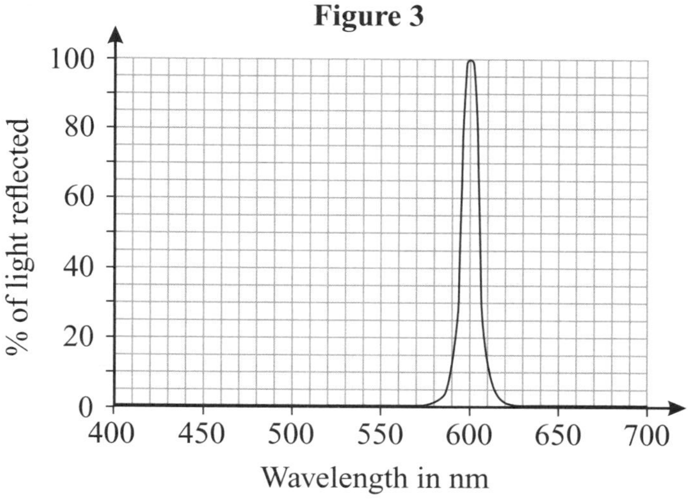

2.1 Determine the colour of the paint. Use a calculation to support your answer.
     The speed of light is 3.0×10^8 m/s.

Colour = ...

[4]

2.2 Household paint consists of a solid, powdery pigment held together by a liquid binder.
     The binder becomes a smooth solid when it dries. Suggest why the ratio of binder to pigment is higher in glossy paints than in matte paints. Explain your answer.

....

....

....

....

....

....

....

[3]

[Total 7 marks]

Topic 6 — Waves

3 Radio waves are commonly used in communications on Earth.

3.1 Gamma radiation can pass through most obstacles, which would be useful in communications.
Suggest **one** reason why gamma radiation isn't used in communications.

....

....
[1]

A scientist uses a radio wave transmitter to create radio waves. He connects an oscilloscope to a radio wave receiver to detect the radio waves created. The oscilloscope is set up to display the potential difference across the receiver against time. The potential difference across the receiver is directly proportional to the current through the receiver.
Figure 4 shows the trace the scientist sees on the oscilloscope display.
The width of each square on the oscilloscope trace is equal to 2×10^{-6} s.

Figure 4

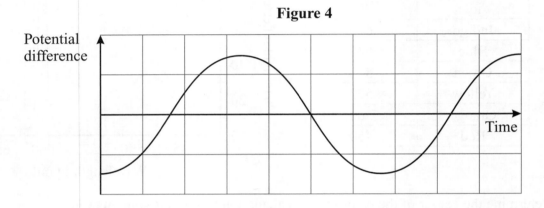

3.2 Using **Figure 4**, calculate the frequency of the radio waves received.

Frequency = ... Hz
[4]

3.3 Suggest why the scientist often gets interference when detecting radio waves.

....

....
[1]
[Total 6 marks]

Score:

23

Radiation and Temperature

1 A planet is orbiting a star. Radiation from the star is incident on the surface of the planet's atmosphere. The star transfers 400 J of energy per second to each square meter of the planet's atmosphere. **Figure 1** shows the paths taken by the incident radiation when it reaches the planet.

Figure 1

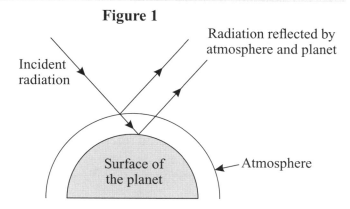

Of the radiation incident on the atmosphere 10% is reflected back into space and 20% is absorbed by the atmosphere. The rest of the radiation passes through the atmosphere to the surface of the planet. The radiation that reaches the surface of the planet is either reflected or absorbed. The ratio of radiation absorbed by the surface of the planet to the radiation reflected by the planet is 5:2.

You may assume that each unit of radiation transfers the same amount of energy, and any energy radiated from the atmosphere towards the surface of the planet is negligible.

1.1 Calculate the amount of energy absorbed by 1 m² of the surface of the planet each second.

Energy = ... J

[2]

1.2 A moon that orbits the planet passes between the star and the planet, causing an eclipse. Suggest the effect this will have on the surface temperature of the planet. Explain your answer.

....

....

....

....

[2]

[Total 4 marks]

Score:

4

Exploring Structures Using Waves

1   Seismic waves can be classified as either P-waves or S-waves.

Figure 1

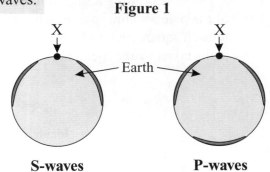

An earthquake occurs at point X. **Figure 1** shows where S-waves and P-waves are detected on the Earth's surface after the earthquake. Areas where waves are detected are shown by the shaded regions. Observations from earthquakes have led us to believe that the Earth has a layered interior structure consisting of a solid inner core surrounded by a liquid outer core, which is surrounded by a solid mantle.

S-waves   **P-waves**

1.1* By comparing the properties of P-waves and S-waves, explain how we now know the Earth is made up of different layers. You should refer to **Figure 1** in your answer.

....

....

....

....

....

....

....

[4]

Figure 2 shows the distance travelled by a P-wave against time as it travels through the Earth. The wave travels through the mantle, passes through the outer core and then travels back into the mantle.

Figure 2

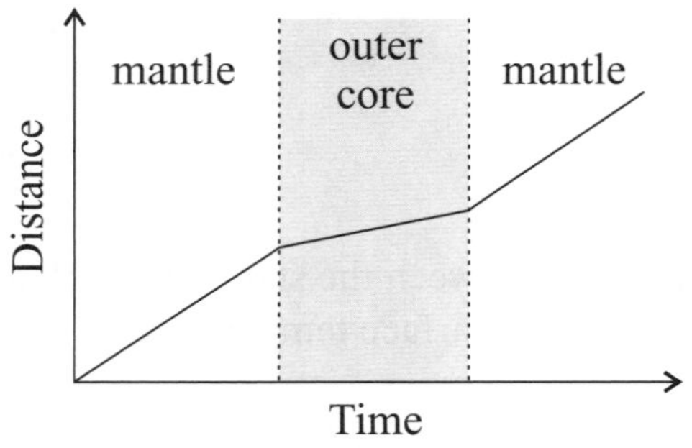

mantle   outer core   mantle

Distance

Time

1.2   Explain what happens to the direction of travel of the wave when it passes into and out of the outer core.

....

....

....

....

[2]

[Total 6 marks]

2* Fake gold bars can be made by covering a bar of tungsten with a thin layer of gold. It is impossible to distinguish their weight from that of a real gold bar.

Explain how ultrasound can be used to test whether a gold bar is genuine or fake. Include in your answer what results you would expect if the bar was solid gold and if the bar had a tungsten core.

....

....

....

....

....

....

....

....

....

[Total 4 marks]

3 Ultrasound can be used by ships to find the depth of the sea beneath them.

The maximum depth of the English Channel is 175 m. A ship located above the deepest part of the English Channel uses an ultrasound machine to direct a pulse of ultrasound to the sea floor. An echo is received at the ship 0.23 seconds after the initial pulse was sent.

A different point in the English Channel has a depth of 63 m. Calculate how long it would take for a pulse of ultrasound to travel from the surface of this point of the English Channel to the sea floor and back again. Give your answer to two significant figures.

Time taken = ... s

[Total 5 marks]

Score:

15

Topic 6 — Waves

Magnetism and Electromagnetism

1   Before digital ammeters were invented, analogue ammeters were used instead.
Analogue ammeters are based on a device called a moving-coil galvanometer.
The basic design of a moving-coil galvanometer is shown in **Figure 1**.

Figure 1

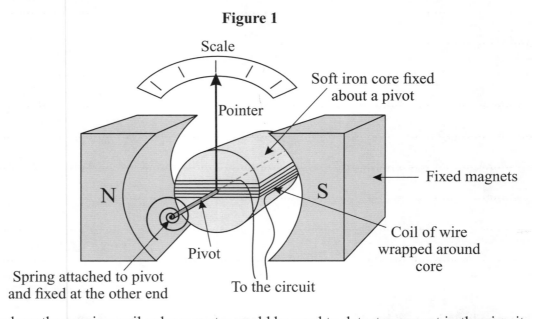

1.1* Explain how the moving-coil galvanometer could be used to detect a current in the circuit.
Include an explanation of what happens when the current is increased, removed and reversed.

....

....

....

....

....

....

....

....

....

....

[6]

Figure 2 shows the magnetic field lines between two flat magnets and two curved magnets.

Figure 2

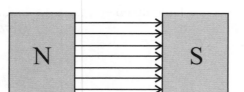 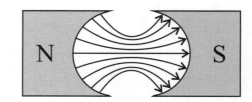

1.2 Suggest why curved magnets are used for a moving-coil galvanometer. Explain your answer.

....

....

....

[2]

1.3 **Figure 3** shows a front-end view of the coil used in **Figure 1** and the direction of the current in the coil. Draw the field lines of the magnetic field caused by the current in the coil.

Figure 3

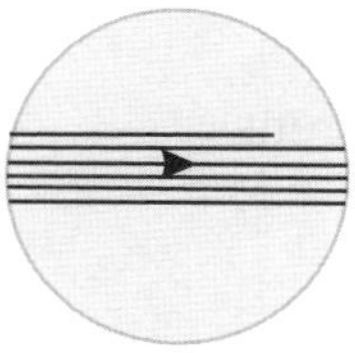

[2]

1.4 The length of the side of the coil in **Figure 1** is 25 mm. When the coil carries a current of 2 A, the force on one wire along the side of the coil is 10 mN. Calculate the magnetic flux density of the magnetic field of the permanent magnets. Give the unit.

Magnetic flux density = ... Unit = ...

[4]

1.5 A student is building their own moving-coil galvanometer. They need to calibrate the scale so that it reads the correct value when a current is applied. Suggest how they could do this.

....

....

[1]

1.6 When the student tries to measure a larger current, the pointer moves off the end of the scale. What **two** changes could the student make to the equipment to allow the galvanometer to measure larger currents on the same sized scale?

1. ....

2. ....

[2]

[Total 17 marks]

Topic 7 — Magnetism and Electromagnetism

The Generator Effect and Transformers

1 Transformers are used in the national grid to change the potential difference and current of the electricity supply.

1.1 Which combination of potential difference and current should be used in the national grid to transmit electricity efficiently and effectively? Tick **one** box.

Low potential difference and high current. ☐

Low potential difference and low current. ☐

High potential difference and high current. ☐

High potential difference and low current. ☐

Explain your answer.

....

....

....

....

[4]

1.2 A transformer used in the national grid has 60 000 turns of wire on the primary coil and 45 000 turns of wire on the secondary coil. The input current is 1.2 kA. Calculate the output current.

Current = ... A

[3]

1.3 State **one** assumption you have made in 1.2.

....

[1]

1.4 Explain why transformers do not work with direct current.

....

....

....

....

[3]

[Total 11 marks]

2   Generators use the principles of the generator effect to produce an electric current.
Figure 1 shows two different types of generator, an alternator and a dynamo.

Figure 1

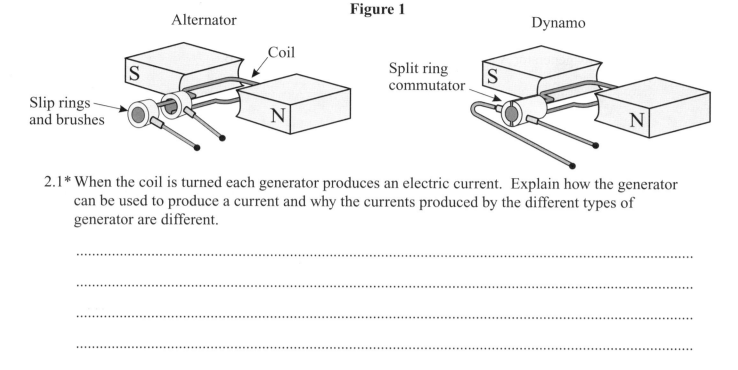

2.1* When the coil is turned each generator produces an electric current. Explain how the generator
can be used to produce a current and why the currents produced by the different types of
generator are different.

....

....

....

....

....

....

....

....

....

....

[6]

Figure 2 shows the output currents from the two different generators.

Figure 2

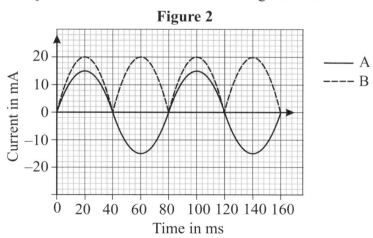

2.2   Explain which line on **Figure 2** shows the output current of the alternator.

....

....

[1]

Topic 7 — Magnetism and Electromagnetism

2.3 Calculate the frequency of the alternator.

Frequency .... Hz

[2]

2.4 Suggest why generator A produces a higher current than generator B.

....

[1]

[Total 10 marks]

3   **Figure 3** shows a magnet being moved into a coil of wire, that is part of a complete circuit.
     A current is induced in the wire. The induced current generates a magnetic field around the coil.

Figure 3

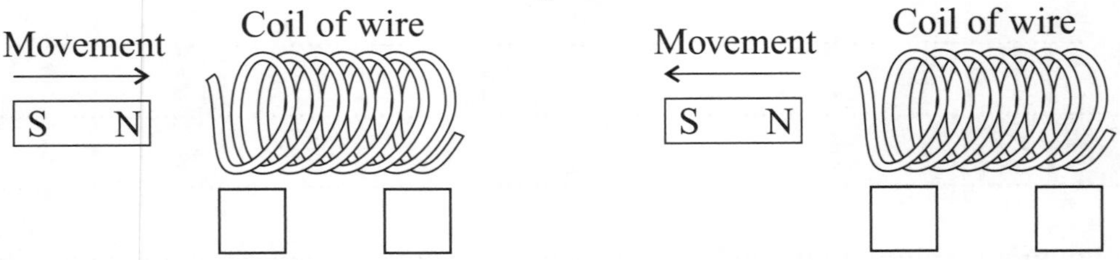

3.1 In the boxes in **Figure 3**, write N or S to show the North and South poles of the coil in each case.

[2]

3.2 **Figure 4** shows a cone attached to a coil of wire. This can be used as part of a
     simple intercom system to convert between sound waves and electrical signals.
     Explain how the equipment in **Figure 4** can be used to convert sound waves into electrical signals.

Figure 4

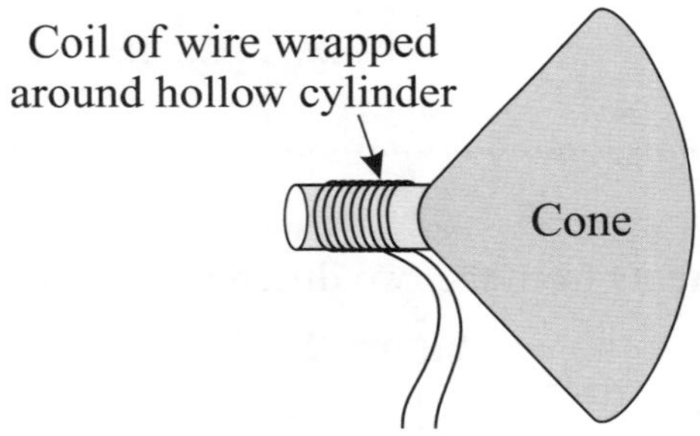

....

....

....

....

....

....

[4]

[Total 6 marks]

Score:

27

Red-Shift and Orbits

1 An astronomer is investigating the visible light from a distant galaxy, galaxy X.
She splits the light observed into a continuous spectrum, known as an absorption spectrum.

In an absorption spectrum, dark lines appear in the spectrum, corresponding to wavelengths
of light absorbed by elements in the galaxy. **Figure 1** shows the same parts of two spectra.
Spectrum A is part of the spectrum of the light obtained by the astronomer on Earth.
Spectrum B is part of the spectrum of light that would be obtained if it was detected immediately
after it was emitted from galaxy X.

Figure 1

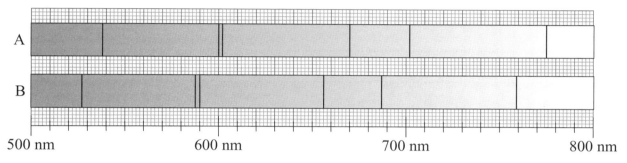

The astronomer observes that the absorption spectra have the same pattern of dark lines,
but that this pattern has been shifted by the time it reaches the Earth. This is red-shift.

1.1 Explain how the behaviour of the universe caused the light from the galaxy to be red-shifted.

....

....

....

....

[2]

The red-shift of a galaxy, z, can be calculated using the equation:

$$z = \frac{\Delta\lambda}{\lambda}$$

Where: λ = the wavelength of a dark line in absorption spectrum B
$\Delta\lambda$ = the difference between λ and the wavelength of the equivalent dark line in
absorption spectrum A

1.2 Using **Figure 1**, calculate the red-shift of galaxy X.
Give your answer to two significant figures.

Red-shift = ...
[4]

Galaxy Y is even further away from Earth than galaxy X. The astronomer knows that, at the point of emission, galaxy Y has an identical absorption spectrum to galaxy X.

She compares the visible light absorption spectrum detected on Earth from galaxy Y with spectrum B. She finds that the absorption lines with the longest wavelengths are missing.

1.3 Explain why the absorption lines are missing from the visible part of the spectrum. Suggest what the astronomer could do to observe the missing absorption lines.

....

....

....

....

....

....

[3]

[Total 9 marks]

2 In the 1600s, Johannes Kepler developed a series of laws for how the planets of the solar system orbit the Sun. These are known as Kepler's laws of planetary motion.

2.1 The planets orbit the Sun in almost circular orbits. Explain how, as a planet orbits the Sun, it can be constantly accelerating while its speed remains constant.

....

....

....

....

[2]

Kepler's Third Law states:

$$T^2 = kr^3$$

Where: T = time taken for a full orbit (the orbital period) in s
k = a constant known as Kepler's constant in s^2/m^3
r = distance from the orbiting object to the object it is orbiting in m

Kepler's Third Law can also be applied to the orbits of moons around planets and dwarf planets. **Table 1** shows data about some of Pluto's moons.

Table 1

Moon	Distance from Pluto (m)	(Distance from Pluto)^3 (m^3)	Orbital period (s)	(Orbital period)^2 (s^2)
Styx	42.4×10^6	7.62×10^{22}	1.74×10^6	3.03×10^{12}
Nix	48.7×10^6	1.16×10^{23}	2.15×10^6	4.62×10^{12}
Kerberos	57.8×10^6	1.93×10^{23}	2.78×10^6	7.73×10^{12}
Hydra	64.7×10^6	2.71×10^{23}	3.30×10^6	1.09×10^{13}

Figure 2 shows an incomplete graph of the square of the orbital period of the moons against the cube of their distance from Pluto.

Figure 2

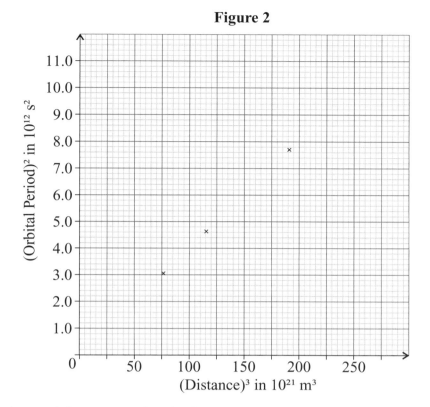

(Distance)³ in 10^{21} m³

2.2 Complete the graph in **Figure 2** by plotting the missing point for Hydra. Draw a line of best fit.

[2]

2.3 Using **Figure 2**, calculate Kepler's constant for objects orbiting Pluto.

Kepler's constant = ... s^2/m^3

[2]

2.4 Some theories suggest that another of Pluto's moons, called Charon, used to orbit Pluto at a smaller distance than its current orbit. Suggest what change occurred, if any, in the speed of Charon's orbit when it moved from its old orbit to its current orbit. Explain your answer.

....

....

....

....

[2]

[Total 8 marks]

Score:

17

Topic 8 — Space Physics

Mixed Questions for Paper 2

1   **Figure 1** shows a golf club hitting a stationary golf ball of mass 45 g.

Figure 1

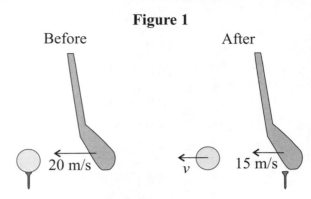

The club has a mass of 0.40 kg and travels at 20 m/s before hitting the ball. Immediately after hitting the ball, the club slows down to 15 m/s.

1.1   Calculate the size of the velocity of the ball immediately after it has been hit. Give your answer to two significant figures.

Velocity = ... m/s
[5]

1.2   The ball lands on the ground, then rolls along the ground for 5 s before coming to a stop. The initial velocity of the ball after landing on the ground is 3 m/s. Calculate the size of the average resistive force acting on the ball as it rolls along the ground.

Force = ... N
[4]

1.3   The same golf club is used to hit a second golf ball, also with a mass of 45 g. This new golf ball is designed so that when it's hit by the club, there is a longer contact time compared to the first ball. Assuming that both balls experience the same average force whilst in contact with the club, explain how the balls' velocities will differ immediately after being hit.

....

....

....

....
[2]

[Total 11 marks]

2   Star X is a star orbited by a single planet.

The intensity and wavelength distribution for star X is shown in **Figure 2**. Star X is assumed to be a black body.

Figure 2

The equation that links the peak wavelength of a black body, λ_{peak}, to its temperature, T is:

$$\lambda_{peak} T = 2.9 \times 10^{-3}$$

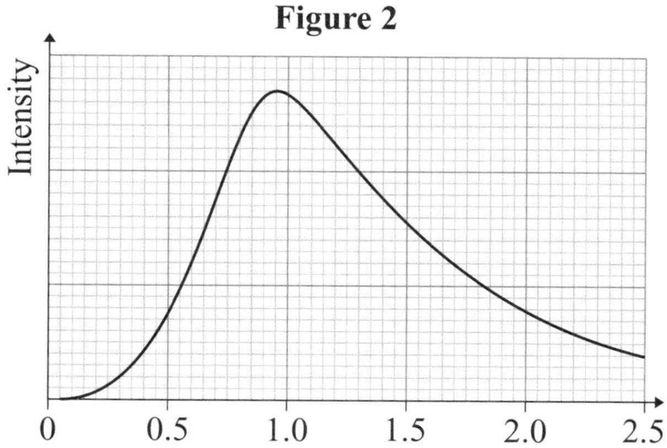

where λ_{peak} is in metres and T is in kelvin.
Temperatures can be converted from kelvin to Celsius using the equation:

Temperature (°C) = Temperature (K) – 273

2.1 Calculate the temperature of star X in °C. Give your answer to two significant figures.

Temperature = ... °C
[5]

2.2 The intensity and wavelength distribution for star X was measured on Earth.
The intensity and wavelength distribution for another star, star Y, was also measured on Earth.
Star Y is closer to Earth than star X.
Star X and star Y are the same temperature.
Suggest why star Y has a shorter peak wavelength.

....

....
[1]

2.3 The average diameter of the planet's orbit around star X is approximately 7.5 million km.
Each orbit takes 11.2 days. Calculate the average orbital speed of the planet.
Give your answer to two significant figures.

Average orbital speed = ... m/s
[4]

[Total 10 marks]

Mixed Questions for Paper 2

3 A boy skims a stone across a lake. **Figure 3** shows the velocity-time graph for the vertical component of the stone's velocity from the time it first touches the water.

Figure 3

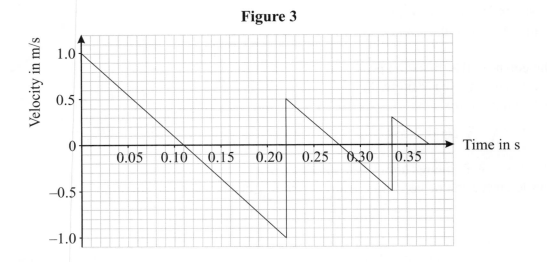

3.1 Describe the motion of the stone between 0.11 s and 0.22 s.

....

....
[2]

3.2 Determine the maximum height the stone reached after touching the water.

Height = ... m
[2]

3.3 The stone settles on the lake floor. Light travels through water more slowly than it travels through air. Complete **Figure 4** to show the ray of light from the Sun reflecting from the stone and back out of the water.

Figure 4

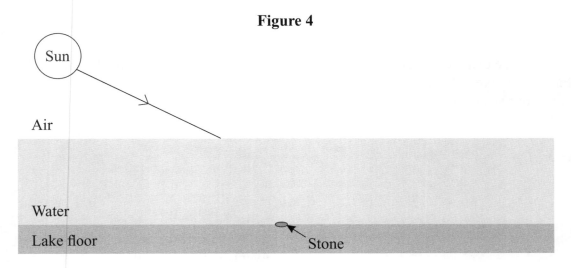

[2]
[Total 6 marks]

4   A train is shown in **Figure 5**. The train driver spots a hazard and pushes a button that triggers the emergency brake. A diagram of the train's emergency brake system is shown in **Figure 6**.

Figure 5

Figure 6

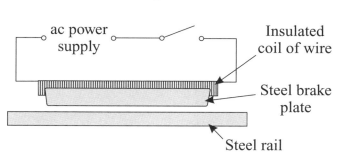

4.1* The coil and brake plate are mounted on the train above the rails and can move up or down.
     When the driver presses the button, the switch closes.
     Explain how pressing the button causes the train to come to a stop.

     ....

     ....

     ....

     ....

     ....

     ....

     ....

     ....

     ....

[4]

4.2 The train has a mass of 200 000 kg and is travelling at 28 m/s before the button is pressed.
     The emergency brakes provide a constant resultant force of 0.4 MN on the train.
     Calculate the braking distance of the train.

Braking distance = ... m

[5]

[Total 9 marks]

Mixed Questions for Paper 2

5 A miner is working in a tunnel. The only light in the tunnel comes from a red light. The red light is a white bulb which is covered by a red transparent filter. The miner wears a helmet which appears blue in sunlight.

5.1 Explain why the bulb appears to be red and what effect this has on the appearance of the miner's helmet.

....

....

....

....
[2]

Once she is a safe distance away, the miner sets off explosives in the tunnel. Seismic waves created by the explosives are recorded at a nearby earthquake-monitoring station. The station uses equipment to measure the amplitude of the waves over time. The results are shown in **Figure 7**.

Figure 7

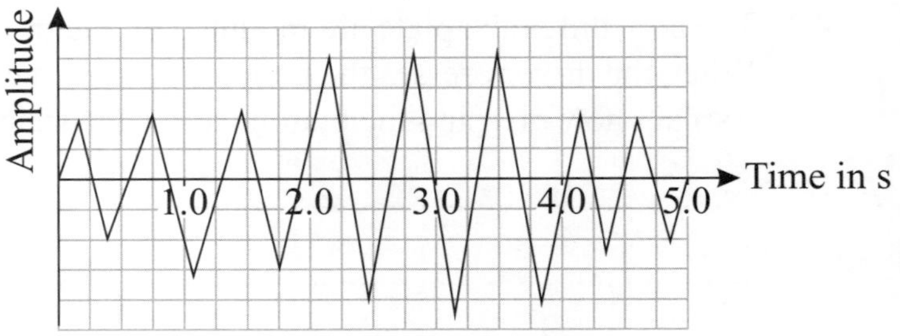

5.2 The seismic waves travel through the Earth at an average speed of 6400 m/s. Calculate the average wavelength of the seismic waves.

Average wavelength = ... m
[4]

5.3 The seismic waves reached the station 1.4 s after the explosion. Sound waves generated by the explosion travel through the air and are heard by a person 2.1 km away from the mine. Which of the following statements is true? Tick **one** box.

The person hears the explosion before the seismic waves are detected at the station. ☐

Seismic waves are detected at the station before the person hears the explosion. ☐

The person hears the explosion at the same time as the seismic waves are detected at the station. ☐

[1]
[Total 7 marks]

Exam Practice Tip

If you get an answer wrong, make sure you study the correct answer and work out what you haven't understood. Then go back and brush up on that topic again, rather than just learning the answer for one specific scenario — you'll probably need to apply the knowledge differently next time.

Score: ☐

43

Answers

Topic 1 — Energy

Page 1: Energy Transfers

1.1 mass of stone, m_s = 20 g = 20 ÷ 1000 = 0.02 kg
mass of box = 100 g = 100 ÷ 1000 = 0.1 kg
total mass of box and stone, m_T = 0.1 + 0.02 = 0.12 kg
height of swing = 20 cm = 20 ÷ 100 = 0.2 m
$E_p = m_T gh$ = 0.12 × 9.8 × 0.2 = 0.2352 J
energy transferred to g.p.e. stores of box and stone = energy transferred from kinetic energy store of the stone, $E_p = E_k$
$E_k = \frac{1}{2}m_s v^2$
$v = \sqrt{\dfrac{2\,E_k}{m_s}} = \sqrt{\dfrac{2 \times 0.2352}{0.02}}$
  = 4.8497... m/s
  = **4.8 m/s (to 2 s.f.)**
[6 marks for correct answer, otherwise 1 mark for correct substitution into equation for gravitational potential energy, 1 mark for correct calculation of energy in gravitational potential energy store, 1 mark for correct rearrangement of the kinetic energy equation, 1 mark for correct substitution into the kinetic energy equation and 1 mark for correct unrounded answer]

1.2 The energy transferred is nine times larger than the first time.
[1 mark]
The initial extension was one times the original length, and the new extension is three times the original length. Because the extension has been tripled, and the energy in the elastic potential energy store is proportional to the square of the extension, the energy transferred is nine times larger.

Pages 2-5: Specific Heat Capacity, Power and Efficiency

1.1 Draw a tangent at (2000, 27)
E.g.

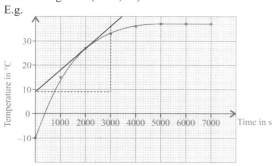

rate of temperature change = gradient of tangent = $\dfrac{36 - 9}{3000 - 0}$
= **0.009 °C/s**
(Accept any answer between 0.0085 °C/s and 0.0095 °C/s)
[3 marks for correct answer, otherwise 1 mark for correctly drawn tangent and 1 mark for attempt to calculate gradient]

1.2 $\Delta E = mc\Delta\theta$
Replace change in temperature with rate of temperature change to find rate of energy transfer.
So, rate of energy transfer = mass × specific heat capacity × rate of temperature change
= 2.0 × 1800 × 0.009
= **32.4 J/s**
[2 marks for correct answer, otherwise 1 mark for correct substitution]
Even if you got the answer to 1.1 wrong, you get full marks for 1.2 if you did the calculations correctly using your answer for 1.1.

1.3 Find the total input energy transferred to the freezer:
power = energy transferred ÷ time, so:
energy transferred = power × time
20.0 minutes = 20.0 × 60 = 1200 s
so total input energy transfer = 250 × 1200 = 300 000 J
efficiency = $\dfrac{\text{useful output energy transfer}}{\text{total input energy transfer}}$
efficiency = 95% = 0.95
useful output energy transfer = efficiency × total input energy transfer
    = 0.95 × 300 000
    = **285 000 J**
[5 marks for correct answer, otherwise 1 mark for correct substitution into energy transferred equation, 1 mark for correct calculation of total input energy transfer, 1 mark for correct rearrangement of efficiency equation and 1 mark for correct substitution into efficiency equation]
OR:
Find the useful power output of the freezer:
efficiency = $\dfrac{\text{useful power output}}{\text{total power input}}$
efficiency = 95% = 0.95
useful power output = efficiency × total power input
    = 0.95 × 250
    = 237.5 W
Then find the useful output energy transferred in 20.0 minutes:
energy transferred = power × time
20.0 minutes = 20.0 × 60 = 1200 s
so energy transferred = 237.5 × 1200 = **285 000 J**
[5 marks for correct answer, otherwise 1 mark for correct rearrangement of the efficiency equation, 1 mark for correct substitution into efficiency equation, 1 mark for correct calculation of useful power output and 1 mark for correct substitution into energy transferred equation]

2.1 Find the rate at which energy is wasted, i.e. the wasted power, in order to find total power input:
power = energy transferred ÷ time
wasted power = energy wasted ÷ time
time = 9 × 60 = 540 s
wasted power = 300 ÷ 540 = 0.555... W
useful power output = 0.1 × 1000 = 100 W
total power input = useful power output + wasted power
    = 100 + 0.555... = 100.555... W
efficiency = $\dfrac{\text{useful power output}}{\text{total power input}}$
  = $\dfrac{100}{100.555...}$
  = 0.994475...
  = **0.99 (= 99%) (to 2 s.f.)**
[6 marks for correct answer, otherwise 1 mark for correct substitution into power equation, 1 mark for correct calculation of wasted power, 1 mark for correct calculation of total power input, 1 mark for correct substitution into efficiency equation and 1 mark for correct unrounded answer]
OR:
Find the useful output energy transferred:
power = energy transferred ÷ time, so:
energy transferred = power × time
time = 9 × 60 = 540 s
power = 0.1 × 1000 = 100 W
useful output energy transferred = 100 × 540 = 54 000 J
total input energy transfer = useful output energy transfer + wasted energy
    = 54 000 + 300 = 54 300 J

$$\text{efficiency} = \frac{\text{useful output energy transfer}}{\text{total input energy transfer}}$$
$$= \frac{54\,000}{54\,300}$$
$$= 0.994475...$$
$$= \mathbf{0.99\ (= 99\%)\ (to\ 2\ s.f.)}$$

[6 marks for correct answer, otherwise 1 mark for correct substitution into power equation, 1 mark for correct calculation of useful output energy transfer in 9 mins, 1 mark for correct calculation of total input energy transfer, 1 mark for correct substitution into efficiency equation and 1 mark for correct unrounded answer]

2.2 Draw a line of best fit, e.g.

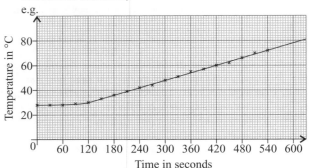

10 mins in seconds = $10 \times 60 = 600$ s

Evaluate temperature at 600 s,

Temperature = **78 °C (Accept between 76 °C and 80 °C)**

[2 marks for correct answer, otherwise 1 mark for suitably drawn line of best fit with a constant positive gradient between 120 s and 600 s]

2.3 From line of best fit:

Change in temperature between 180 s and 540 s = $72 - 36$
$$= 36\ °C$$

Time taken for temperature change = $540 - 180 = 360$ s

Useful power of heater = 0.1 kW = $0.1 \times 1000 = 100$ W

Energy transferred = power × time, so:

Energy transferred in 360 s = $100 \times 360 = 36\,000$ J

$\Delta E = mc\Delta\theta$, so $c = \dfrac{\Delta E}{m\Delta\theta}$

$$c = \frac{36\,000}{6 \times 36}$$
$$= 166.666...\ J/kg°C$$
$$= \mathbf{167\ J/kg°C\ (to\ 3\ s.f.)}$$

(Accept between 162 J/kg°C and 171 J/kg°C)

[6 marks for correct answer, otherwise 1 mark for evaluating two temperatures from your line of best fit at least 240 s apart, 1 mark for correct substitution into energy transferred equation, 1 mark for correct calculation of the energy transferred, 1 mark for correct substitution into specific heat capacity equation and 1 mark for correct unrounded answer]

Even if you got the gradient in 2.2 wrong, you get full marks for 2.3 if you did the calculations correctly using your gradient from 2.2.

2.4 A higher thermal conductivity would mean energy would be transferred at a higher rate from the lead to the surroundings *[1 mark]*. This means the temperature of the lead would increase at a lower rate, which would give a higher value of specific heat capacity *[1 mark]* as more energy is transferred for a given increase in temperature / specific heat capacity is inversely proportional to temperature change *[1 mark]*.

3.1 47.5 MJ = 4.75×10^7 J

$\Delta E = mc\Delta\theta$, so $c = \dfrac{\Delta E}{m\Delta\theta}$

$$c = \frac{4.75 \times 10^7}{3000 \times 4.0}$$
$$= 3958.333...\ J/kg°C$$
$$= \mathbf{3960\ J/kg°C\ (to\ 3\ s.f.)}$$

[4 marks for correct answer, otherwise 1 mark for correct rearrangement, 1 mark for correct substitution and 1 mark for correct unrounded answer]

3.2 Find the total input energy transferred to the solar panel by the Sun:

power = energy transferred ÷ time, so:

energy transferred = power × time

time = 12 hours = $12 \times 60 \times 60 = 43\,200$ s

power = 5 kW = $5 \times 1000 = 5000$ W

energy transferred = $5000 \times 43\,200 = 2.16 \times 10^8$ J

$$\text{efficiency} = \frac{\text{useful output energy transfer}}{\text{total input energy transfer}}$$
$$= \frac{4.75 \times 10^7}{2.16 \times 10^8}$$
$$= 0.21990...$$
$$= \mathbf{0.22\ (= 22\%)\ (to\ 2\ s.f.)}$$

[5 marks for correct answer, otherwise 1 mark for correct substitution into energy transferred equation, 1 mark for correct calculation of energy transferred, 1 mark for correct substitution into efficiency equation and 1 mark for correct unrounded answer]

Page 6: Energy Resources

1.1 How to grade your answer:

Level 0: There is no relevant information. *[No marks]*

Level 1: There are some relevant points but they are basic or unclear. Mentions a benefit and a drawback for using more wind power, or makes a comparison of wind and coal in at least one area. *[1 to 2 marks]*

Level 2: There is a description referring to at least one benefit and one drawback of using more wind power and how this compares to using coal. The points made have some detail, but may not be linked. *[3 to 4 marks]*

Level 3: There is a clear and detailed description referring to both benefits and drawbacks of using more wind power and how they compare to using coal. The answer refers to reliability and environmental factors. *[5 to 6 marks]*

Here are some points your answer may include:

Benefits:

Using more wind power will be more sustainable for the future, as wind is renewable and can be replenished/will not run out, but coal is non-renewable and can't be replenished/will run out.

Using more wind and less coal to generate electricity will reduce the harm done to the environment, such as the amount of pollutants released into the atmosphere.

Using wind to generate electricity does not produce carbon dioxide but burning coal does.

Carbon dioxide contributes to the greenhouse effect/climate change/global warming.

Using wind to generate electricity does not release sulfur dioxide but burning coal does.

Sulfur dioxide contributes to acid rain, which can be harmful to trees and soils and can have far-reaching effects in ecosystems.

Wind does not need to be mined, but coal does, which can destroy habitats and changes the landscape.

Drawbacks:

Using more wind than coal to generate electricity may cause electricity supply issues.

Wind is less reliable than coal as power cannot be generated when it isn't windy / it is too windy, whereas coal is currently always in stock, and can be burnt at any time to produce energy.

Wind power cannot be increased to meet demand, whereas a coal-fuelled power station can be made to increase its power by burning coal at a greater rate.

Using more wind than coal to generate electricity may also raise economic and social issues.

It costs money to build new wind turbines and connect them to the national grid, but it does not cost any extra to continue using existing coal plants.

Wind turbines may be noisy, which can disrupt local residents and wildlife.

Wind turbines are considered by some people to be an eyesore.

1.2   To find the total percentage greater than 10 m/s, multiply the height of each bar to the right of 10 m/s by its width, then add them all together:

Percentage time = $(7 \times 2) + (5 \times 4) + (2 \times 4) + (1 \times 4)$
= **46%**

[2 marks for correct answer, otherwise 1 mark for correctly reading widths and heights of the correct bars from the graph]

Topic 2 — Electricity

Pages 7–9: Circuits

1.1 $Q = It$
$t = 2.0$ hours $= 2.0 \times 60 \times 60 = 7200$ s
$Q = 0.50 \times 7200 = 3600$ C
Divide the total charge that passes through the thermistor by the charge on one electron to find the number of electrons:

Number of electrons $= \dfrac{3600}{1.6 \times 10^{-19}}$
$= \mathbf{2.25 \times 10^{22}}$

[3 marks for correct answer, otherwise 1 mark for correct substitution into Q = It and 1 mark for dividing the total charge by the charge of an electron]

1.2   Find the potential difference across the resistor, V_2, and use this to find the current in the circuit:
$V_2 = V_{total} - V_1 = 6 - 0.25 = 5.75$ V
$V = IR$, so:
$I = \dfrac{V_2}{R_2} = \dfrac{5.75}{1.0} = 5.75$ A

Use the current in the circuit and V_1 to find the resistance of the thermistor:
$R_1 = \dfrac{V_1}{I} = \dfrac{0.25}{5.75}$
$= 0.043478...\ \Omega = \mathbf{0.0435\ \Omega}$ **(to 3 s.f.)**

[6 marks for correct answer, otherwise 1 mark for correct calculation of V₂, 1 mark for correct substitution to find current through circuit, 1 mark for correct calculation of current, 1 mark for correct substitution to find R₁ and 1 mark for correct unrounded answer]

1.3   The heater should be connected across the thermistor, as when the external temperature decreases, the thermistor's resistance increases *[1 mark]* and so the potential difference across the thermistor increases *[1 mark]*. As they would be connected in parallel, the potential difference across the heater would be equal to the potential difference across the thermistor, so the heater would get hotter as the temperature decreased *[1 mark]*.

2.1   Line of best fit is a straight line, so it has an equation of the form $y = mx + c$,
where $y = R$, $m =$ gradient, $x = L$, and $c = y$-intercept.
Line goes through origin, so $c = 0$.
$m =$ gradient $= \dfrac{\text{change in } y}{\text{change in } x}$
E.g. $m = \dfrac{54 - 0}{5.4 - 0} = 10$
So, equation of line is $R = 10\,L$
[2 marks for correct answer, otherwise 1 mark for correct calculation of the gradient]

Make sure you calculate the gradient from changes in y and x that cover at least half of the line of best fit.

2.2   Calculate resistance of length of wire:
$R = 10\,L$,
so $R = 10 \times 0.375$
$= 3.75\ \Omega$
Calculate current through wire:
$V = IR$ so $I = V \div R$
$V = 0.5$ kV $= 0.5 \times 1000 = 500$ V
$I = 500 \div 3.75$
$= 133.333...$ A
$= \mathbf{133\ A}$ **(to 3 s.f.)**

[5 marks for correct answer, otherwise 1 mark for correct calculation of resistance of wire, 1 mark for correct rearrangement of V = IR, 1 mark for correct substitution to find current and 1 mark for correct unrounded answer]

Even if you got the answer to 2.1 wrong, you get full marks for 2.2 if you did the calculations correctly using your answer for 2.1.

2.3   3 Ω *[1 mark]*

For a 1.2 m length of the first wire, the resistance is 12 Ω. The cross-sectional area of the second wire is 4 times larger so, since resistance is inversely proportional to cross-sectional area, divide the first wire's resistance by 4.

3.1   How to grade your answer:
Level 0:   There is no relevant information. *[No marks]*
Level 1:   There are some relevant points but the response is unclear. There is some comparison of the readings on the ammeters at different potential differences, but the explanation of any difference is vague or unclear. *[1 to 2 marks]*
Level 2:   There is a comparison of the readings on the ammeters as the potential difference of the power supply increases, with a clear explanation of how and why the values differ from each other. Points made are valid and clearly linked with their explanations. *[3 to 4 marks]*

Here are some points your answer may include:
In parallel circuits, the current is split between branches.
More current flows down paths with lower resistance, since each branch has the same potential difference and current is inversely proportional to resistance.
The reading on A_1 is initially lower than the reading on A_2, because the bulb has a lower resistance.
As the potential difference of the power supply increases, the total current through the circuit increases.
The resistance of the resistor is constant for all values of current.
As the potential difference across the bulb increases, its resistance increases.
As the resistance of the bulb increases, it will receive a smaller fraction of the total current.
At the potential difference when the bulb and resistor have equal resistances, the readings on A_1 and A_2 will be equal.
If the potential difference of the power supply is increased past this point, the bulb's resistance will become greater than the resistor's.
So the reading on A_1 will be greater than the reading on A_2.

3.2   The total resistance of the circuit is equal to the sum of the resistances of the resistor and component X *[1 mark]*. As potential difference increases, the current through component X increases more for a given increase in potential difference (as shown by the increasing gradient of the graph) so the resistance of the component decreases *[1 mark]*. So as potential difference of the power supply increases, the total resistance of the circuit decreases *[1 mark]*.

Pages 10–12: Electrical Appliances and the National Grid

1.1 Power is equal to the gradient of the graph, so instantaneous power is greatest when gradient of graph is steepest.
So time of greatest power = 25 s
Draw a tangent at 25 s,
E.g.

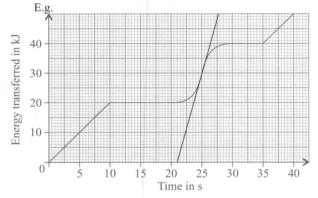

$$\text{power} = \text{gradient of tangent} = \frac{48\,000 - 0}{27.5 - 21} = 7384.615...$$

$$= \textbf{7380 W (to 3 s.f.)}$$

(Accept between 6380 W and 8380 W)
[4 marks for correct answer, otherwise 1 mark for correctly drawn tangent at 25 s, 1 mark for attempt to calculate the gradient of the tangent and 1 mark for correct unrounded answer]

1.2 $E = QV$
Energy transferred between 20 s and 30 s = 40 kJ – 20 kJ
$$= 20 \text{ kJ}$$
$$= 20 \times 1000$$
$$= 20\,000 \text{ J}$$

$V = E \div Q$
$$= 20\,000 \div 12$$
$$= 1666.66... \text{ V}$$
$$= \textbf{1700 V (to 2 s.f.)}$$
[5 marks for correct answer, otherwise 1 mark for correct energy values read from the graph, 1 mark for correct rearrangement, 1 mark for correct substitution and 1 mark for correct unrounded answer]

1.3 $P = I^2R$
Resistance = 250 mΩ = 250 ÷ 1000 = 0.25 Ω

$$I = \sqrt{\frac{P}{R}} = \sqrt{\frac{36}{0.25}} = \textbf{12 A}$$
[3 marks for correct answer, otherwise 1 mark for correct rearrangement and 1 mark for correct substitution]

1.4 7.56 units worth of energy = $7.56 \times 3.6 \times 10^6$
$$= 2.7216 \times 10^7 \text{ J}$$

$E = Pt$ so $t = E \div P$
$t = (2.7216 \times 10^7) \div 36 = 7.56 \times 10^5$ s
Number of hours = $7.56 \times 10^5 \div (60 \times 60)$
$$= \textbf{210 hours}$$
[5 marks for correct answer, otherwise 1 mark for correct calculation of total energy wasted, 1 mark for correct rearrangement of power equation, 1 mark for correct substitution into power equation and 1 mark for correct time in seconds]

2.1 Power of electricity supplied to the transformer = 1.843 GW
= 1.843×10^9 W

Power of electricity leaving transformer = $\frac{99}{100} \times 1.843 \times 10^9$
$$= 1.824... \times 10^9 \text{ W}$$

$P = VI$, so
$V = P \div I$
$I = 166$ kA = $166 \times 1000 = 166\,000$ A

$V = 1.824... \times 10^9 \div 166\,000$
$$= 10\,991.3855... \text{ V}$$
$$= \textbf{11\,000 V (to 3 s.f.)}$$
[5 marks for correct answer, otherwise 1 mark for correct calculation of power of electricity leaving transformer, 1 mark for correct rearrangement for potential difference, 1 mark for correct substitution for potential difference and 1 mark for correct unrounded answer]

2.2 Find energy transferred when the current flows:
$E = Pt$
$P = 0.31$ GW = $0.31 \times 10^9 = 3.1 \times 10^8$ W
$E = 3.1 \times 10^8 \times 0.55 = 1.705 \times 10^8$ J
$E = QV$, so to find charge:
$Q = E \div V$
$V = 380$ kV = $380 \times 1000 = 3.8 \times 10^5$ V
$Q = (1.705 \times 10^8) \div (3.8 \times 10^5)$
$$= 448.684... \text{ C}$$
$$= \textbf{450 C (to 2 s.f.)}$$
[6 marks for correct answer, otherwise 1 mark for correct substitution to find energy transferred, 1 mark for correct calculation of energy transferred, 1 mark for correct rearrangement for charge, 1 mark for correct substitution for charge and 1 mark for correct unrounded answer]
OR
Find current that flows through the cable:
$P = VI$, so $I = P \div V$,
$P = 0.31$ GW = $0.31 \times 10^9 = 3.1 \times 10^8$ W
$V = 380$ kV = $380 \times 1000 = 3.8 \times 10^5$ V
so $I = 3.1 \times 10^8 \div 3.8 \times 10^5 = 815.78...$ A
Find charge that is transferred in 0.55 s:
$Q = It$
$$= 815.78... \times 0.55$$
$$= 448.684... \text{ C}$$
$$= \textbf{450 C (to 2 s.f.)}$$
[6 marks for correct answer, otherwise 1 mark for correct rearrangement for current, 1 mark for correct substitution to find current, 1 mark for correct calculation of current, 1 mark for correct substitution for charge and 1 mark for correct unrounded answer]

2.3 The person is at 0 V, so there will be large potential difference between the car and the person *[1 mark]*. Charge in the car could jump from the car to the person, causing a large current to flow through the person, giving them a large electric shock which could injure or kill them *[1 mark]*.

Page 13: Static Electricity

1.1 How to grade your answer:
Level 0: There is no relevant information. *[No marks]*
Level 1: There are some relevant points but the response is unclear. Mentions either the transfer of charge or the cause of the force between the objects. *[1 to 2 marks]*
Level 2: There is a detailed explanation of the transfer of negative charge and the generation of electric fields, and how the interaction of these fields gives rise to the force between the objects which gets smaller with increasing distance between the objects. The points made are clear and coherently linked together. *[3 to 4 marks]*
Here are some points your answer may include:
The insulating objects have become electrically charged.
This is because negatively charged electrons have been rubbed off one object and transferred to the other.
The insulating object that gains electrons becomes negatively charged.
The insulating object that loses electrons has an equal positive charge.
Since the objects are now charged, an electric field is generated around each of them.
The objects' electric fields interact.

This interaction causes them to exert a non-contact force on each other.

Since the objects have opposite charge they will attract.

The electric fields get weaker with distance from each of the charged objects.

So the further apart the objects are moved, the smaller the force of attraction between them.

1.2

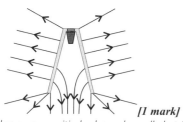

[1 mark]

The gold leaves are positively charged, so all electric field lines are pointing away from the gold leaves.

Topic 3 — Particle Model of Matter

Page 14: Density

1.1   Rearrange $\rho = m \div V$ for V:

$V = m \div \rho$

Calculate the total volume of the block of aerogel:

$V = 0.50 \div 1.50 = 0.333...\ \text{m}^3$

Divide the volume below the waterline by the total volume and multiply by 100 to get the percentage of the volume beneath the waterline:

percentage of volume $= \dfrac{5 \times 10^{-4}}{0.333...} \times 100 = \textbf{0.15\%}$

[4 marks for correct answer, otherwise 1 mark for correctly rearranging $\rho = m \div V$ for V, 1 mark for correct substitution into $V = m \div \rho$ and 1 mark for correctly calculating the total volume of the aerogel]

1.2 $\rho = m \div V$

Rearranging for m gives:

$m = \rho \times V$

mass produced in 24 hours $= \rho \times V$

         $= 1.50 \times 0.360$

         $= 0.54\ \text{kg}$

minutes in one day $= 24 \times 60 = 1440$ minutes

rate of production $=$ mass $\div$ time

         $= 0.54 \div 1440$

         $= 0.000375\ \text{kg/min}$

Convert kg/min to g/min:

$0.000375 \times 1000 = \textbf{0.375 g/min}$

[5 marks for the correct answer, otherwise 1 mark for correctly rearranging $\rho = m \div V$ for m, 1 mark for correct substitution into $m = \rho \times V$, 1 mark for correctly calculating the mass of aerogel produced in 24 hours and 1 mark for dividing this mass by the number of minutes in a day]

Pages 15-17: Internal Energy and Changes of State

1.1   The change in temperature of the water is:

$30 - 27 = 3\ °\text{C}$

The energy transferred from the ball to the water is:

$\Delta E = mc\Delta\theta$

     $= 1.0 \times 4200 \times 3$

     $= 12\ 600\ \text{J}$

Rearrange the equation for $\Delta\theta$:

$\Delta\theta = \dfrac{\Delta E}{mc}$

$50\ \text{g} = 50 \div 1000 = 0.05\ \text{kg}$

The ball loses 12 600 J, so the change in temperature of the ball is:

$\Delta\theta = \dfrac{\Delta E}{mc} = \dfrac{12\ 600}{0.05 \times 900} = 280\ °\text{C}$

The water and ball end up at the same temperature of 30 °C, so the initial temperature of the ball is:

$30 + 280 = \textbf{310 °C}$

[5 marks for the correct answer, otherwise 1 mark for the correct substitution into $\Delta E = mc\Delta\theta$, 1 mark for calculating the energy transferred from the ball to the water, 1 mark for correct substitution into $\Delta\theta = \dfrac{\Delta E}{mc}$ and 1 mark for correct calculation of the change in temperature of the ball]

1.2

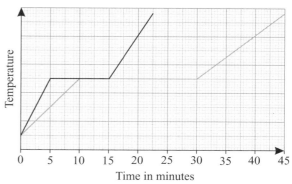

[1 mark for correctly drawn line]

The energy needed to change the temperature and state of a substance is proportional to its mass. Since ball B has half the mass of ball A, half the energy is needed to change the temperature and state of ball B (compared to ball A) *[1 mark]*. Energy is transferred to ball B at the same constant rate as ball A, so the amount of energy needed for these changes will be supplied in half the time *[1 mark]*. The melting point is the same for both ball A and ball B, as the two balls are made from the same material, so the flat section of the graph must be at the same temperature *[1 mark]*.

2.1 $\Delta E = mc\Delta\theta$

Rearranging for m gives:

$m = \dfrac{\Delta E}{c\Delta\theta} = \dfrac{740}{217 \times 30} = 0.113... = \textbf{0.11 kg (to 2 s.f.)}$

[4 marks for the correct answer, otherwise 1 mark for correct rearrangement, 1 mark for correct substitution and 1 mark for the correct unrounded answer]

2.2   The tin is changing state *[1 mark]*. Energy is being used to break the intermolecular bonds rather than raise the temperature/energy is transferred to the potential energy stores of the particles rather than their kinetic energy stores *[1 mark]*.

2.3 $30\ \text{g} = 30 \div 1000 = 0.03\ \text{kg}$

The change in temperature of the liquid ammonia is:

$-33 - (-60) = 27\ °\text{C}$

The energy needed to raise the temperature of the liquid ammonia is:

$E = mc_l\Delta\theta_l = 0.03 \times 4700 \times 27 = 3807\ \text{J}$

The change in temperature of the gaseous ammonia is:

$-10 - (-33) = 23\ °\text{C}$

The energy needed to raise the temperature of the gaseous ammonia is:

$E = mc_g\Delta\theta_g = 0.03 \times 2060 \times 23 = 1421.4\ \text{J}$

The total energy supplied is equal to the sum of the energy used to raise the temperature of the liquid ammonia, the energy used to boil the ammonia, and the energy needed to raise the temperature of the gaseous ammonia:

$46.3\ \text{kJ} = 46.3 \times 1000 = 46\ 300\ \text{J}$

So the energy used to boil the ammonia

         $= 46\ 300 - 3807 - 1421.4$

         $= 41\ 071.6\ \text{J}$

68

$E = mL$

Rearranging for L gives:

$L = E \div m = 41\ 071.6 \div 0.03$

$= 1\ 369\ 053.3...$

$= \mathbf{1\ 370\ 000\ J/kg\ (to\ 3\ s.f.)}$

$(= \mathbf{1.37 \times 10^6\ J/kg})$

[6 marks for correct answer, otherwise 1 mark for correct substitution into $E = mc_l \Delta \theta_l$ or $E = mc_g \Delta \theta_g$, 1 mark for correctly calculating the energy needed to raise the temperature of the liquid ammonia, 1 mark for correctly calculating the energy needed to raise the temperature of the gaseous ammonia, 1 mark for correct substitution into $L = E \div m$ and 1 mark for calculating the correct unrounded answer]

3.1   It is used to find the mass of chocolate melted due to energy transferred from the surroundings. *[1 mark]*

3.2   The chocolate in the right-hand beaker has melted purely due to the temperature of the surroundings. The masses of the two beakers are the same, so the amount of chocolate that melts due to the heater alone is:

$210 - 90 = 120\ g = 120 \div 1000 = 0.12\ kg$

The energy supplied by the heater is:

$E = Pt = 60 \times 90 = 5400\ J$

Rearrange $E = mL$ for L:

$L = E \div m = 5400 \div 0.12 = \mathbf{45\ 000\ J/kg}$

[5 marks for the correct answer, otherwise 1 mark for correct substitution into $E = Pt$, 1 mark for correctly calculating the energy supplied by the heater, 1 mark for correct rearrangement of $E = mL$ and 1 mark for correct substitution into $L = E \div m$]

Pages 18-19: Particle Motion in Gases

1.1   The pressure outside an underwater air bubble decreases as it rises, so the pressure inside the bubble is greater than the pressure outside the bubble *[1 mark]*. The volume inside the bubble increases until the pressure inside the bubble is equal to the pressure outside / the force acting outwards on the bubble is greater than the forces acting inwards on the bubble, so the volume of the bubble increases *[1 mark]*.

1.2   Use Figure 1 to read off values for the pressure.

Pressure at depth of 10 m = p_1 = 2 kPa

Pressure at depth of 25 m = p_2 = 3.5 kPa

pV = constant so $p_1 V_1 = p_2 V_2$

Rearrange $p_1 V_1 = p_2 V_2$ for V_2:

$V_2 = p_1 V_1 \div p_2 = (2 \times 1000) \div 3.5 = 571.42...$

$= \mathbf{570\ cm^3\ (to\ 2\ s.f.)}$

[4 marks for the correct answer, otherwise 1 mark for reading the correct values from the graph, 1 mark for correct use of pV = constant and 1 mark for correct unrounded answer]

The units for pressure and volume don't need to be converted here since the equation is a ratio.

2.1   The outward force acting on the walls of the cylinder is equal to the sum of the forces exerted by all the particles in the cylinder on the cylinder walls *[1 mark]*. The outward gas pressure is equal to the net force acting per unit area on the cylinder walls *[1 mark]*. If there are fewer oxygen particles in the cylinder, then the particles hit the walls less often, so the net force and pressure will also decrease *[1 mark]*.

2.2   How to grade your answer:

Level 0:   There is no relevant information. *[No marks]*

Level 1:   The explanation given lacks detail and clarity. A link is made between increase in height and the decrease in the energy in the kinetic energy stores of the oxygen particles. *[1 to 2 marks]*

Level 2:   There is a clear and detailed explanation of why the pressure in an oxygen tank decreases with height, and how this is linked to the decrease in the energy in the kinetic energy stores of the oxygen particles. *[3 to 4 marks]*

Here are some points your answer may include:

As the oxygen cylinder is carried up the mountain, the temperature of the oxygen decreases.

The average amount of energy in the kinetic energy stores of the oxygen particles is proportional to their temperature.

So the oxygen particles have a lower average energy in their kinetic energy stores.

The energy in the kinetic energy store of an oxygen particle is proportional to its speed squared.

So the average speed of the oxygen particles decreases as the cylinder is carried higher up the mountain.

As the particles are travelling more slowly, they hit the walls with less force and less often.

This means that the outward force acting on the cylinder due to the oxygen particles decreases.

The pressure acting on the walls of the cylinder is equal to the net force per unit area.

The area of the cylinder remains the same and the net force decreases as the cylinder is carried up the mountain, so the pressure must also decrease.

Topic 4 — Atomic Structure

Pages 20-23: The Atomic Model and Nuclear Radiation

1.1   Beta decay *[1 mark]*.

1.2 $^{93}_{39}Y \rightarrow\ ^{93}_{40}Zr +\ ^{0}_{-1}e$

[2 marks for the correct answer, otherwise 1 mark for correct symbol for a beta particle or 1 mark for all the atomic and mass numbers correct]

1.3   E.g. The mass number has decreased by 4, so the nucleus has lost 4 nucleons. This means the particle emitted was an alpha particle *[1 mark]*. The nucleus has lost 2 protons and 2 neutrons *[1 mark]*.

1.4 $55 - 2 = 53$ *[1 mark]*

When a caesium nucleus emits an alpha particle to become iodine, it loses two protons, so its atomic number decreases by 2.

1.5   Calcium *[1 mark]*

In fusion, lighter elements fuse together to form heavier elements. Calcium is the only element with a lower atomic number than titanium in the list, so it's the only lighter element than titanium.

1.6   There are different isotopes of some elements. Isotopes have the same atomic number but different mass numbers so an element doesn't have one fixed mass number. *[1 mark]*

2.1   35 counts per minute *[1 mark, accept any answer between 32 cpm and 37 cpm]*

2.2

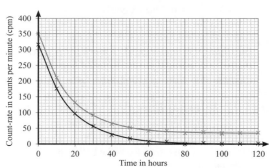

[2 marks for all points and line correctly plotted, otherwise 1 mark for all points being 35 cpm below the original curve]

Even if you got the answer to 2.1 wrong, you get full marks for 2.2 if you drew the correct curve using your answer for 2.1.

2.3   12 hours

Use the curve you drew in 2.2 and work out the time taken for the count-rate to half, e.g. from 315 cpm to 157.5 cpm.

[2 marks for correct answer found from the graph with background radiation removed, otherwise 1 mark for calculating an incorrect value for half life using the correct method but the original uncorrected graph]

2.4 Since the measurements are accurate to ± 5 cpm, the count rate will definitely be below 25 if the corrected count rate is below 20 cpm *[1 mark]*.
The water is safe to drink after 49 hours *[1 mark — accept any value between 48-50]*.

2.5 Radioactivity is a random process. A single reading below 25 cpm does not necessarily indicate that the count-rate will stay below 25 cpm *[1 mark]*.

3.1 Gamma radiation *[1 mark]*.

3.2 The gamma radiation should be directed through the blade towards the detector *[1 mark]*. The blade will reduce the amount of radiation reaching the detector *[1 mark]*. When there is a crack, less radiation will be absorbed and the count rate detected will increase, so the crack can be detected *[1 mark]*.

4.1 $^{131}_{53}\text{I} \rightarrow {}^{131}_{54}\text{Xe} + {}^{0}_{-1}\text{e}$
[2 marks for the correct answer, otherwise 1 mark for correct symbol for a beta particle or 1 mark for all the atomic and mass numbers correct]
$^{131}_{54}\text{Xe} \rightarrow {}^{131}_{54}\text{Xe} + \gamma$
[2 marks for the correct answer, otherwise 1 mark for correct symbol for gamma radiation or 1 mark for all the atomic and mass numbers correct]

4.2 Any two from: e.g. Iodine-131 decays to release gamma radiation which is penetrative enough to be detected outside of the body *[1 mark]*. / Iodine-131 doesn't give out alpha radiation, which would be very dangerous inside the body *[1 mark]*. / Iodine-131 doesn't have a really short half-life, which means that the sample will still emit radiation once it is in the patient, so it can be traced/a diagnosis can be made *[1 mark]*.

4.3 The gamma (or beta) radiation given out by the iodine-131 could pass out of the patient's body and irradiate others nearby *[1 mark]*. Radiation can damage cells and so could cause damage to the people nearby *[1 mark]*.

5.1 How to grade your answer:
Level 0: There is no relevant information. *[No marks]*
Level 1: There is a basic description of contamination and irradiation, but no comparison or discussion of the risk for each type of radiation. Or there is a basic suggestion of how the protective suit protects against contamination and irradiation. Detail and key points are lacking.
[1 to 2 marks]
Level 2: There is a description of contamination and irradiation and an attempt to compare the risk for each type of radiation. There is a basic suggestion of how the protective suit protects against contamination and irradiation. Key points are mentioned but detail may be lacking.
[3 to 4 marks]
Level 3: A detailed description and explanation is provided. The answer contains examples of how the risk of contamination and irradiation differs for each type of radiation, and a full explanation of how the protective suit protects against contamination and irradiation. *[5 to 6 marks]*
Here are some points your answer may include:
The workers are at risk of contamination if the uranium-235 gets onto their skin or if they breathe it in.
They are also at risk of irradiation if they are exposed to radiation.
The risk posed by contamination is high as uranium-235 emits alpha particles which do a lot of damage inside the body.
Gamma radiation isn't as dangerous inside the body as alpha radiation.
The risk posed by irradiation is also high because uranium-235 emits gamma radiation which can easily penetrate deep into the body from outside and damage organs / tissues.
Alpha particles cannot penetrate the body so gamma radiation is more dangerous outside of the body.
The radiation shielding material helps to protect against irradiation as some radiation will be blocked/absorbed before it reaches the body.
The breathing mask protects against contamination as it stops the worker breathing in any radioactive particles in the air.
The protective gloves protect against contamination as they stop radioactive particles getting on the worker's hands.
The sealed zips protect against contamination as they stop any radioactive particles getting into the protective suit.
The sealed zips ensure that there are no gaps in the radiation shielding suit, so they protect against irradiation.

5.2 $^{235}_{92}\text{U} + {}^{1}_{0}\text{n} \rightarrow {}^{92}_{36}\text{Kr} + {}^{141}_{56}\text{Ba} + 3{}^{1}_{0}\text{n}$ *[1 mark]*
The first option cannot be correct as fission is a chain reaction, more neutrons need to be released along with the products. The second option cannot be correct as the nucleus has to absorb a neutron to undergo fission.

Mixed Questions for Paper 1

Pages 24-28: Mixed Questions for Paper 1

1.1 Use $\rho = m \div V$ to calculate the density of a neutron star:
$\rho = (2.1 \times 10^{30}) \div (1.4 \times 10^{13})$
$= 1.5 \times 10^{17}$ kg/m^3
Rearrange $\rho = m \div V$ for m:
$m = \rho V$
$= 1.5 \times 10^{17} \times 1.0 \times 10^{-6}$
$= \mathbf{1.5 \times 10^{11}}$ **kg**
[5 marks for the correct answer, otherwise 1 mark for correct substitution into $\rho = m \div V$, 1 mark for the correct value of ρ for a neutron star, 1 mark for rearranging the equation for m and 1 mark for correct substitution into $m = \rho V$]

1.2 E.g. Solid matter on Earth is made of atoms closely packed together, which are mostly empty space *[1 mark]*. Neutrons do not contain this empty space and so have more mass per unit volume *[1 mark]*.

1.3 The number of seconds in one year is:
$60 \times 60 \times 24 \times 365 = 3.1536 \times 10^7$ s
Calculate the energy released by the Sun in one year:
$(4 \times 10^{26}) \times 3.1536 \times 10^7 = 1.26144 \times 10^{34}$ J
So the number of years it would take the Sun to release 1×10^{44} J is:
$(1 \times 10^{44}) \div (1.26144 \times 10^{34}) = 7.92... \times 10^9$
$= \mathbf{8 \times 10^9}$ **years (to 1 s.f.)**
[3 marks for the correct answer, otherwise 1 mark for dividing 1×10^{44} by the amount of energy released by the Sun in either a year or a second and 1 mark for correctly converting to years from seconds at some point in the calculation]

1.4 The energy from the nearby star is transferred to the kinetic energy stores of the particles of the gas cloud *[1 mark]*, which causes the particles to move faster and so to collide more often / to collide with more force *[1 mark]*. This results in an increase in pressure in the gas cloud *[1 mark]*.

2.1 The useful energy transferred by the lift is the energy transferred to the gravitational potential energy stores of the lift and its contents.

Total mass of lift plus contents = 1200 + 700 = 1900 kg

$E_p = mgh = 1900 \times 9.8 \times 300 = 5\,586\,000$ J

Efficiency = useful output energy transfer ÷ total input energy transfer

9310 kJ = 9310 × 1000 = 9 310 000 J

So efficiency = 5 586 000 ÷ 9 310 000 = **0.6 (= 60%)**

[4 marks for the correct answer, otherwise 1 mark for correct substitution into $E_p = mgh$, 1 mark for calculating the energy transferred to the gravitational potential energy stores of the lift and its contents and 1 mark for correct substitution into the efficiency equation]

2.2 Using $P = E \div t$:

The input power of the service lift is double that of the tourist lift so it transfers twice as much energy per unit time *[1 mark]*. However $E_p = mgh$ and the maximum mass is four times higher for the service lift, so it has to transfer four times as much energy to raise the lift *[1 mark]*. Using $t = E \div P$ shows that the service lift takes twice as long to be raised by a fixed height as the tourist lift *[1 mark]*. So the service lift is two times slower / half the speed of the tourist lift *[1 mark]*.

OR

Using $P = E \div t$,

P_s, E_s and t_s are the power of, energy transferred by and time taken to raise the service lift by a fixed amount.

P_t, E_t and t_t are the power of, energy transferred by and time taken to raise the tourist lift by a fixed amount.

$P_s = 2P_t$ *[1 mark]*

However $E_p = mgh$ and g and h are fixed.

Since the mass of the service lift and its contents is four times that of the tourist lift, $E_s = 4E_t$ *[1 mark]*

Combine these to get $t_s = \dfrac{E_s}{P_s} = \dfrac{4E_t}{2P_t} = 2t_t$ *[1 mark]*

So the service lift is two times slower / half the speed of the tourist lift *[1 mark]*.

2.3 Using $P = VI$:

$I = \dfrac{P}{V} = \dfrac{75}{120} = 0.625$ A

$P = I^2R$ so $R = \dfrac{P}{I^2} = \dfrac{75}{(0.625)^2} = $ **192 Ω**

[5 marks for the correct answer, otherwise 1 mark for substituting into $P = VI$, 1 mark for correct value of I, 1 mark for rearranging $P = I^2R$ and 1 mark for substituting into rearranged equation]

You could also use V = IR to calculate the resistance once you have used P = VI to calculate the current.

2.4 Assuming that the coin has no initial velocity, so no energy in its kinetic energy stores before it starts falling, and that there is no energy lost due to friction/air resistance to the surroundings:

Energy in the coin's gravitational potential energy store at the top = energy in the coin's kinetic energy store at the bottom

$mgh = \dfrac{1}{2}mv^2$

Cancel m from both sides:

$gh = \dfrac{1}{2}v^2$

$v = \sqrt{2gh} = \sqrt{2 \times 9.8 \times 300} = 76.68... = $ **77 m/s (to 2 s.f.)**

[5 marks for the correct answer, otherwise 1 mark for equating the energy in the gravitational potential energy store of the coin at the top with the energy in the kinetic energy store of the coin at the bottom and stating the correct assumptions, 1 mark for correct rearrangement of the equation, 1 mark for correct substitution and 1 mark for correct unrounded answer]

You could also use $v^2 - u^2 = 2as$ to calculate the final speed of the coin.

3.1 How to grade your answer:

Level 0: There is no relevant information. *[No marks]*

Level 1: There is one advantage and disadvantage for either solar arrays or nuclear generators. Detail is lacking. Key points e.g. nuclear waste may be missing. *[1 to 2 marks]*

Level 2: There is one advantage and disadvantage for both solar arrays and nuclear generators. Detail may be lacking in places but key points e.g. nuclear waste should be mentioned. *[3 to 4 marks]*

Level 3: There are several advantages and disadvantages described in detail for both solar arrays and nuclear generators. All key points are covered. *[5 to 6 marks]*

Here are some points your answer may include:

Advantages of nuclear generator:

They have a longer lifetime meaning they won't limit the lifetime of the ISS.

It can produce power in any conditions.

Disadvantages of nuclear generator:

Nuclear waste would have to be stored securely on board.

There is a risk of irradiating the astronauts if the nuclear waste is not stored properly.

There is a risk of an accident occurring which could release a lot of radiation near Earth / into the ISS.

The nuclear reactor needs fuel to run, which would either need to be launched with the ISS or delivered.

A nuclear reactor is quite complex and therefore it may need maintenance.

When the ISS is decommissioned the nuclear reactor will have to be safely brought back to Earth in a crash landing which will be difficult / dangerous to humans on Earth.

Advantages of solar cells:

There is no fuel needed.

There are no radiation safety concerns associated with it.

There is no pollution or waste.

During orbit the ISS regularly gets direct sunlight (i.e there are no clouds to block the sunlight).

The solar cells are less complex and will require less maintenance.

Disadvantages of solar cells:

No electricity can be generated when the ISS is in the shadow of the Earth, this could be a problem in the case of an emergency.

Their lifetime is much shorter and could limit the lifetime of the ISS.

3.2 Rearrange $\rho = m \div V$ for m:

$m = \rho V$

$= 680 \times 0.5 = 340$ kg

$\Delta E = mc\Delta\theta$

$= 340 \times 4600 \times 5 = 7\,820\,000 = $ **7 800 000 J (to 2 s.f.)**

[5 marks for the correct answer, otherwise 1 mark for rearranging $\rho = m \div V$ for m, 1 mark for the correct substitution into this equation, 1 mark for the correct value of m and 1 mark for correct substitution into the equation for energy]

3.3 $V = IR$ so $I = V \div R = 240 \div 0.96 = 250$ A

The ISS spends half of its orbit exposed to sunlight:

90 ÷ 2 = 45 minutes

Convert the time the cells spend exposed to sunlight into seconds:

45 × 60 = 2700 s

$Q = It = 250 \times 2700 = $ **675 000 C**

[5 marks for the correct answer, otherwise 1 mark for correct substitution into $I = V \div R$, 1 mark for correct value of I, 1 mark for correct substitution into $Q = It$ and 1 mark for giving the correct unit]

Answers

3.4 E.g. one source of background radiation is cosmic rays from space, which are absorbed by the atmosphere *[1 mark]*. Where the ISS is positioned in space, there are more cosmic rays since there's no atmosphere to absorb them, so the background radiation on board the ISS is significantly higher than in Cornwall *[1 mark]*. High up in the atmosphere on a plane in flight, there are slightly more cosmic rays than on Earth because less have been absorbed by the atmosphere, so the background radiation is slightly higher than in Cornwall *[1 mark]*.

3.5 Astronauts and pilots both receive a higher radiation dose as a result of being at work *[1 mark]*. Their dose must be measured to make sure it's not too high, as a high dose can increase their risk of developing cancer *[1 mark]*.

4.1 Increasing the number of secondary fissions caused by each fission in the chain reaction. *[1 mark]*

Energy is released when an atom undergoes fission, so increasing the number of fissions increases the energy released.

4.2 Iodine-131 is dangerous when inhaled or ingested as beta radiation is ionising and can cause damage to the body internally *[1 mark]*. If this iodine were absorbed by the thyroid, it would remain in the body for a long time / travel around the body in molecules made by the thyroid *[1 mark]*. Ingesting a potassium iodide tablet with a stable iodine isotope allows the thyroid to absorb enough iodine in the form of a stable isotope, preventing the radioactive iodine-131 from being absorbed by the thyroid *[1 mark]*. The stable iodine does no harm and the iodine-131 is then removed from the body, which minimises the time that the ionising radiation spends in the body and so minimises damage through irradiation *[1 mark]*.

Topic 5 — Forces

Pages 29-32: Forces and Work Done

1.1 Resultant force = upwards forces – downwards forces
$$= 40.0 \times 10^6 - (7.60 \times 10^6 + 9.40 \times 10^6)$$
$$= 23 \times 10^6 \text{ N}$$

So need to draw a 23 mm arrow pointing upwards, e.g.:

[1 mark for arrow drawn from the × and pointing directly upwards, 1 mark for the line being 23 mm in length]

1.2 Find the gravitational field strength of the Earth's gravitational field at the Moon:

$$g = \frac{GM_E}{r^2} = \frac{(6.67 \times 10^{-11}) \times (5.97 \times 10^{24})}{(3.84 \times 10^8)^2} = 0.00270... \text{ N/kg}$$

$W = m \times g$
so $m = W \div g$
$m = 1.98 \times 10^{20} \div 0.00270...$
$\quad = 7.3320... \times 10^{22}$
$\quad = \mathbf{7.33 \times 10^{22} \text{ kg (to 3 s.f.)}}$

[6 marks for correct answer, otherwise 1 mark for correct substitution into gravitational field strength equation, 1 mark for correct calculation of gravitational field strength, 1 mark for correct rearrangement of weight equation, 1 mark for correct substitution into weight equation and 1 mark for correct unrounded answer]

2.1 Total energy transferred by adult = total work done by adult
Energy transferred to gravitational potential energy stores
$$= 5.44 \text{ kJ} = 5.44 \times 1000 = 5440 \text{ J}$$
So, total work done by adult = 5440 + 2270 = 7710 J
$W = Fs$, rearrange for F:
$F = W \div s$
$\quad = 7710 \div 105$
$\quad = 73.4285...$
$\quad = \mathbf{73.4 \text{ N (to 3 s.f.)}}$

[5 marks for correct answer, otherwise 1 mark for correct calculation of total work done by adult, 1 mark for correct rearrangement of work done equation, 1 mark for correct substitution into work done equation and 1 mark for correct unrounded answer]

2.2 E.g. using scale of 1 cm = 100 N

Construct a closed triangle, and measure the length of the weight vector. Convert the length to force using the scale.
Weight = 7.2 cm = 7.2 × 100 = **720 N**
(Accept between 715 N and 725 N)
[3 marks for correct answer with suitable scale diagram, otherwise 1 mark for arrows drawn with a suitable scale and 1 mark for 3 arrows drawn with correct lengths in a closed triangle]

3.1 How to grade your answer:
Level 0: There is no relevant information. *[No marks]*
Level 1: There are some relevant points, but the answer is unclear. Some comment is made on why rope B is more suited, with reference to the spring constant or the elastic limit. *[1 to 2 marks]*
Level 2: There is a clear and detailed explanation of why rope B is better suited, which includes a comparison of the materials' spring constants and elastic limits. *[3 to 4 marks]*

Here are some points your answer may include:
Under the average weight of a person, rope A extends by around 0.06 m, while rope B only extends by around 0.025 m.
This means that rope A may extend past the maximum allowed extension of 7 cm (0.07 m) when used by a person of above average weight, while rope B will not.
The gradient of the linear part of a force-extension graph is equal to the spring constant, since the linear part of the graph is defined by $F = ke$.
The gradient of the linear part of rope B's graph is greater than that of rope A, so it has a greater spring constant.
This means rope B will extend less under a given force, and extend less for the same increase in force.
So rope B's extension will be more consistent over a range of weights.
Rope A reaches its elastic limit at 800 N.
This is close to the average weight of a person, so the rope could deform permanently when a person's weight is applied.
This means the rope swing would have to be replaced (as it has permanently changed shape).
Rope B does not reach its elastic limit until around 1400 N, so it can safely support a wide range of human weights.

3.2 First find the spring constant of rope B.

The gradient of the straight line part of the force-extension graph is equal to the spring constant, k.

E.g. so $k = \dfrac{\text{change in } y}{\text{change in } x} = \dfrac{1120 - 0}{0.040 - 0} = 28\,000$ N/m

work done to stretch spring = energy transferred to elastic potential energy store

$E_e = \frac{1}{2}ke^2$

Rearrange for extension:

$e = \sqrt{\dfrac{2E_e}{k}}$

$= \sqrt{\dfrac{2 \times 21.0}{28\,000}}$

$= 0.038729...$

$= \mathbf{0.0387 \ m \ (to \ 3 \ s.f.)}$

[5 marks for correct answer, otherwise 1 mark for correct calculation of spring constant by use of the gradient, 1 mark for correct rearrangement of elastic potential energy equation for extension, 1 mark for correct substitution into the equation to find extension and 1 mark for correct unrounded answer]

4.1 Weight of the plank, $W_p = m_p g = 10 \times 9.8 = 98$ N

Weight of mass at B, $W_B = m_B g = 10 \times 9.8 = 98$ N

Since plank is uniform, weight of plank acts at centre, 3 m from support A.

The distance from support A to support C is twice the distance from C to D, so:

Distance AC = 4.0 m, Distance CD = 2.0 m,

Distance AB = Distance BC = 2.0 m

The weight of the plank acts at 1.0 m from point C.

Let the force applied by support A = F_A

Taking moments about point C, given that the plank is balanced:

clockwise moments = anticlockwise moments

$F_A \times 4.0 = (98 \times 2.0) + (98 \times 1.0)$

$F_A = \dfrac{(98 \times 2.0) + (98 \times 1.0)}{4.0}$

$= \mathbf{73.5 \ N}$

[5 marks for correct answer, otherwise 1 mark for correct calculation of the weights of masses, 1 mark for equating the clockwise and anticlockwise moments about point C, 1 mark for correct substitution into this equation and 1 mark for correct rearrangement to find the force at point A]

4.2 Pressing down on the plank at point D. *[1 mark]*

The mass is the same distance from both pivots, but point D is closer to point C than point A. So more force will be required to lift the mass by pressing down at point D and pivoting about point C.

Pages 33-34: Pressure

1 The plane experiences air resistance/friction as it flies due to collisions with air particles *[1 mark]*. At a high altitude, air density is lower, so there are fewer collisions in a given period of time and the air resistance/friction is decreased *[1 mark]*. The lower the air resistance/friction, the lower the force needed to maintain a constant speed, and so the less fuel used *[1 mark]*.

2.1 Difference in pressure = pressure due to oil + pressure due to water

So, pressure due to oil = difference in pressure – pressure due to water

First calculate the pressure due to water:

Pressure due to column of liquid, $p = h\rho g$

Oil is 2 cm thick, so 5 cm below surface of the oil is 3 cm below surface of the water. 3 cm = 3 ÷ 100 = 0.03 m.

Pressure due to water = $0.03 \times 1000 \times 9.8 = 294$ Pa

Difference in pressure = 470.4 Pa

So, pressure due to oil = 470.4 – 294 = 176.4 Pa

Rearrange pressure equation for density:

$\rho = \dfrac{p}{hg}$

Thickness of oil = 2 cm = 2 ÷ 100 = 0.02 m

$\rho = \dfrac{176.4}{0.02 \times 9.8} = \mathbf{900 \ kg/m^3}$

[5 marks for correct answer, otherwise 1 mark for correct substitution into pressure equation to find pressure due to water, 1 mark for correct calculation of pressure due to water, 1 mark for correct rearrangement of pressure equation for density and 1 mark for correct substitution to find density of oil]

2.2

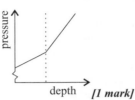

[1 mark]

Oil is less dense than water, and pressure is directly proportional to density, so the pressure increases with depth at a greater rate in oil compared to water.

3.1 $p = \dfrac{F}{A}$

Pressure inside the aerosol can = 500 kPa

$= 500 \times 1000 = 500\,000$ Pa

Height of aerosol can = 20 cm = 20 ÷ 100 = 0.2 m

Radius of aerosol can = 2.5 cm = 2.5 ÷ 100 = 0.025 m

Surface area of aerosol can = $(2 \times \pi \times 0.025) \times (0.025 + 0.2)$

$= 0.03534... \ m^3$

Rearrange pressure equation for F:

$F = p \times A$

$= 500\,000 \times 0.03534...$

$= 17\,671.45... \ N$

$= \mathbf{17\,700 \ N \ (to \ 3 \ s.f.)}$

[5 marks for correct answer, otherwise 1 mark for correct calculation of surface area, 1 mark for correct rearrangement of pressure equation, 1 mark for correct substitution into pressure equation and 1 mark for correct unrounded answer]

3.2 The upthrust acting on the can is equal to the weight of water displaced by the can *[1 mark]*. Since the density of the can and its contents is less than the density of water, this upthrust is greater than the weight of the can *[1 mark]*. So when the can is released, it will experience a resultant force upwards *[1 mark]* which causes it to float towards the surface *[1 mark]*.

Pages 35-36: Motion

1.1 Total distance travelled = 740 + 1400 + 360 = 2500 m

Average speed = 27.2 m/s

total distance travelled = average speed × total time taken

so, total time taken = total distance travelled ÷ average speed

$= 2500 ÷ 27.2$

$= 91.9117... \ s$

Time taken for last 360 m = 91.9117... – 27 – 50

$= 14.9117... \ s$

$= \mathbf{14.9 \ s \ (to \ 3 \ s.f.)}$

[4 marks for correct answer, otherwise 1 mark for correct rearrangement of speed equation, 1 mark for correct substitution to find total time taken and 1 mark for correct unrounded answer]

1.2 Speed is the gradient of a *d-t* graph. Maximum speed occurs at point when gradient is greatest, between around 252-264 s. Draw a tangent at this point.
E.g.

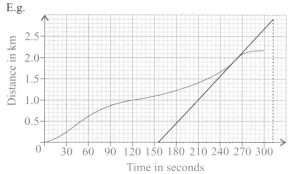

Find the gradient of the tangent:
change in y = 2.9 – 0 = 2.9 km
change in x = 312 – 156 = 156 s
speed = gradient = $\dfrac{\text{change in } y}{\text{change in } x} = \dfrac{2.9}{156} = 0.01858...$ km/s

To convert to km/h, multiply km/s by 60 × 60 = 3600
speed = 0.01858... × 3600 = 66.923... = **67 km/h (to 2 s.f.)**
(Accept between 62 km/h and 72 km/h)
[5 marks for correct answer, otherwise 1 mark for suitable tangent drawn, 1 mark for attempt to calculate gradient, 1 mark for correct calculation of speed in km/s or m/s and 1 mark for correct unrounded answer]

2.1 18.0 knots *[1 mark]*
The maximum speed is 9 m/s.
So the speed in knots is 9 ÷ 0.5 = 18.0 knots.

2.2 average speed = total distance travelled ÷ total time
Distance travelled is given by area under graph.
Each square = 2 × (5 × 60) = 600 m
Number of squares under graph = 31.5
So, area under graph = 31.5 × 600 = 18 900 m
(Accept between 18 600 m and 19 200 m)
time = 50 minutes = 50 × 60 = 3000 s
So, average speed = 18 900 ÷ 3000 = **6.3 m/s**
(Accept between 6.2 m/s and 6.4 m/s)
[4 marks for correct answer, otherwise 1 mark for correct calculation of area of each square, 1 mark for multiplying area of one square by total number of squares and 1 mark for correct substitution into equation for speed]

Pages 37-39: More on Motion

1.1 First find the final speed using the equation $v^2 - u^2 = 2as$
$v = \sqrt{u^2 + 2as} = \sqrt{1^2 + (2 \times 9.8 \times 0.75)} = 3.962...$ m/s
$a = \dfrac{\Delta v}{t}$
so $t = \dfrac{\Delta v}{a} = \dfrac{3.962... - 1}{9.8} = 0.3022... = $ **0.30 s (to 2 s.f.)**
[6 marks for correct answer, otherwise 1 mark for correct rearrangement of equation for final speed, 1 mark for correct substitution to find the final speed, 1 mark for correct calculation of final speed, 1 mark for correct substitution into equation to find time and 1 mark for correct unrounded answer]

1.2 How to grade your answer:
Level 0: There is no relevant information. *[No marks]*
Level 1: Some relevant points are made about the forces acting and the motion of the stone, but it is not clear how the forces relate to the object's motion. *[1 to 2 marks]*
Level 2: There is a description of most of the forces that act on the stone as it falls. An attempt has been made to link these forces to the motion of the stone shown in the graph, but some points are missing. *[3 to 4 marks]*

Level 3: There is a clear and detailed description of the forces that act on the stone as it falls, and how these forces relate to the motion of the stone shown in the graph. Points are made in a sensible order and are clearly linked.
[5 to 6 marks]
Here are some points your answer may include:
The stone begins by accelerating downwards through the air at a constant rate due to its weight.
This is shown by the section of the graph that is a straight line with a positive gradient.
Once the stone enters the water, upthrust and drag act against its motion.
These forces cause the rapid deceleration shown by the steep negative gradient.
The drag on the stone decreases as the stone's speed decreases.
This causes the stone's deceleration to decrease, so the graph becomes less steep.
Eventually the total upwards forces become equal to the weight of the stone.
At this point the acceleration of the stone becomes zero and the speed of the stone is constant.
So the graph becomes a straight horizontal line.

2.1 Inertial mass is the ratio of force ÷ acceleration.
The gradient of the graph is acceleration ÷ force.
Therefore, inertial mass = 1 ÷ gradient.
gradient = $\dfrac{4.0 - 0}{2.0 - 0} = 2$
inertial mass = 1 ÷ 2 = **0.5 kg**
[3 marks for correct answer, otherwise 1 mark for calculation of gradient and 1 mark for attempting to find the inverse of the gradient]

2.2 Read correct acceleration from the line of best fit in Figure 3.
At 1.3 N, a = 2.6 m/s²
$v^2 - u^2 = 2as$, so:
$u = \sqrt{v^2 - 2as} = \sqrt{2.53^2 - (2 \times 2.6 \times 1)}$
$= 1.09585... = $ **1.1 m/s (to 2 s.f.)**
[5 marks for correct answer, otherwise 1 mark for correct value of acceleration from the line of best fit, 1 mark for correct rearrangement, 1 mark for correct substitution and 1 mark for correct unrounded answer]

2.3 For the car to travel at a constant speed, the braking force must equal the force causing it to accelerate down the hill.
$F = ma$
Typical mass of a car ≈ 1000 kg
So, braking force = 1000 × 1.8 = **1800 N**
[3 marks for correct answer, otherwise 1 mark for suitable typical mass of a car and 1 mark for correct substitution]
You'd get full marks here for correct calculations using any suitable value for the mass of a car.

3 The Earth exerts an attractive force on a person equal to their weight *[1 mark]*. Due to Newton's third law, the person must exert an equal and opposite force on the Earth *[1 mark]*. The Earth does not noticeably move towards the person because the Earth has a much higher mass than a person *[1 mark]* and since acceleration is inversely proportional to mass (Newton's second law) the Earth's acceleration towards the person is very small/negligible *[1 mark]*.

Pages 40-42: Stopping Distances and Momentum

1.1   How to grade your answer:

Level 0:   There is no relevant information. *[No marks]*

Level 1:   There is a brief explanation of the general trends of the graphs, but the points made are vague and not well connected. An equation of motion or energy transfer is mentioned, but its link to the graphs is not clear. *[1 to 2 marks]*

Level 2:   There is some explanation of the shapes of the two graphs, with reference to equations of motion and energy changes. Some relevant equations of motion or energy transfers are missing. *[3 to 4 marks]*

Level 3:   There is a clear and detailed explanation of the shapes of the graphs, with reference to equations of motion and energy changes. Points made are clearly linked and all relevant equations of motion and energy transfers are included. *[5 to 6 marks]*

Here are some points your answer may include:

Thinking distance is the distance travelled during the driver's reaction time.

Reaction time does not depend on speed.

So, since distance travelled = speed × time, and time is constant, thinking distance increases linearly with speed.

So the graph of thinking distance is a straight line.

Braking distance is the distance travelled between applying the brakes and coming to a stop.

When a vehicle brakes, the brakes do work to transfer energy away from the kinetic energy store of the vehicle.

Work done = force × distance, and the braking force is assumed to be constant at the maximum force the brakes can apply.

So the braking distance is proportional to the work done by the brakes.

To stop the vehicle, the brakes must do work equal to the energy in the kinetic energy store of the vehicle.

The energy in the vehicle's kinetic energy store = ½ × mass × (speed)².

So braking distance is proportional to the speed of the vehicle squared.

This produces the curved graph of braking distance against speed.

1.2   Convert 33 m/s to mph:

Speed in mph = 33 ÷ 0.447 = 73.8... mph ≈ 74 mph

Evaluate both graphs at 74 mph:

Thinking distance = 22 m

Braking distance = 84 m

Stopping distance = 22 + 84 = **106 m**

[3 marks for correct answer, otherwise 1 mark for correctly converting the speed to mph and 1 mark for correctly reading distance from one of the graphs]

1.3   Thinking distance/reaction time is not affected by road conditions and so the thinking distance graph will remain the same *[1 mark]*. A slippery road means there will be less friction between the tyres and the road once the brakes have been applied *[1 mark]*. This will result in the car travelling further for the same speed *[1 mark]*, so the gradient of the braking distance graph will be greater at all speeds *[1 mark]*.

2.1   First, calculate the final velocity of the ruler when it is caught.

$a = \dfrac{\Delta v}{t}$ so

$\Delta v = at = 9.8 \times 0.20 = 1.96$ m/s

As initial velocity = 0 m/s, the final velocity = 1.96 m/s.

Rearrange $v^2 - u^2 = 2as$, for distance travelled:

$s = \dfrac{v^2 - u^2}{2a} = \dfrac{1.96^2 - 0^2}{2 \times 9.8} = 0.196$ m
$= 0.196 \times 100 = \mathbf{19.6\ cm}$

[5 marks for correct answer, otherwise 1 mark for correct calculation of the final velocity, 1 mark for correct rearrangement for distance travelled, 1 mark for correct substitution to find distance travelled and 1 mark for correct answer in m]

2.2   Any two from: e.g. The ruler could be weighted at the bottom (e.g. with modelling clay) *[1 mark]*. This would ensure that the ruler falls vertically downwards, so distance measured is more accurate *[1 mark]*. / Another person should be present to make sure the ruler is aligned correctly with the thumb before being dropped *[1 mark]*. This will help prevent parallax errors in measuring the starting position of the ruler *[1 mark]*. / Several repeats should be taken and the average reaction time calculated *[1 mark]*. This will help reduce the effect of any random errors in the final result *[1 mark]*.

3.1   Conservation of momentum means that, as the total momentum before firing the rifle is zero, the total momentum after must also be zero *[1 mark]*. Since the bullet has a momentum in one direction, the rifle must have a momentum in the opposite direction in order for the total momentum after to be zero, so the rifle must recoil *[1 mark]*.

3.2   E.g. increase the mass of the rifle *[1 mark]*. Since momentum = mass × velocity, a larger mass will give a smaller velocity for a given momentum *[1 mark]*.

3.3   Let velocity to the right be positive.

For when the bullet is fired from the rifle:

momentum = mass × velocity

total initial momentum = 0

momentum of bullet after = $0.01 \times v_b$

momentum of rifle after = 4.00×-1.00

total momentum before = total momentum after

$0 = (0.01 \times v_b) + (4.00 \times -1.00)$ *[1 mark]*

$v_b = \dfrac{4.00}{0.01}$

$v_b = 400$ m/s *[1 mark]*

For the collision between bullet and wooden block:

Momentum of bullet before = 0.01×400

Momentum of block before = 0.5×0

Momentum of block and bullet after = $(0.01 + 0.5) \times v_B$

Total momentum before = total momentum after

$(0.01 \times 400) + (0.5 \times 0) = (0.01 + 0.5) \times v_B$ *[1 mark]*

$v_B = \dfrac{4}{0.51}$ *[1 mark]*

$= 7.84313... = \mathbf{7.84\ m/s\ (to\ 3\ s.f.)}$ *[1 mark]*

If you get the correct answer here, you'll get the full 5 marks, regardless of whether you've written down all the working shown above.

3.4   The deformable pad increases the time over which the rifle comes to rest after recoiling (by being compressed) *[1 mark]*. Since force is equal to the rate of change of momentum $(F = \Delta(mv)/t)$, this decreases the force on the shoulder *[1 mark]*, and so decreases the risk of injury to the shoulder *[1 mark]*.

Answers

Topic 6 — Waves

Page 43: Investigating Wave Properties

1.1 The distance between ten shadow lines is equal to nine wavelengths, so one wavelength is equal to
$27 \div 9 = 3$ cm $= 0.03$ m
$T = 1 \div f$
Rearrange for f:
$f = 1 \div T$
  $= 1 \div 0.25 = 4$ Hz
$v = f\lambda = 4 \times 0.03 = $ **0.12 m/s**
[5 marks for the correct answer, otherwise 1 mark for calculating the correct wavelength, 1 mark for correct substitution into $f = 1 \div T$, 1 mark for calculating the correct frequency and 1 mark for correct substitution into $v = f\lambda$]

1.2 If the ripple tank was illuminated at an angle, the shadows produced would be distorted/uneven, so it would be difficult to measure the wavelength accurately *[1 mark]*.

1.3 The time interval is 0.25 s *[1 mark]*. The time taken for a wave to travel exactly one wavelength ahead and take the place of the previous wave (and so appear to have not moved) is equal to the period of the wave *[1 mark]*.

Pages 44-46: Electromagnetic Waves and Lenses

1.1
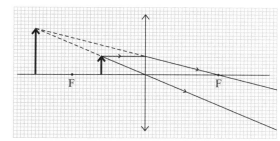

[1 mark for virtual rays drawn correctly, 1 mark for ray drawn through the principal focus then parallel to the axis, 1 mark for ray drawn diagonally through the axis and the lens, 1 mark for object drawn with correct position and size]

1.2 The image is real and upside down. *[1 mark]*

1.3 magnification = image distance ÷ object distance
         $= 0.40 \div 0.16$
         $= 2.5$
magnification = image height ÷ object height
Rearrange for object height:
object height = image height ÷ magnification
         $= 12 \div 2.5$
         $= $ **4.8 cm**
[5 marks for correct answer, otherwise 1 mark for correct substitution into magnification = image distance ÷ object distance, 1 mark for correctly calculating the magnification of the lens, 1 mark for correct rearrangement of magnification = image height ÷ object height, and 1 mark for correct substitution into object height = image height ÷ magnification]

2.1 100% of the light with a wavelength of 600 nm is reflected. This wavelength corresponds to the colour of the paint.
$v = f\lambda$
Rearrange for f:
$f = v \div \lambda$
  $= (3.0 \times 10^8) \div (600 \times 10^{-9})$
  $= 5 \times 10^{14}$ Hz (or 500 THz)
From the table, this frequency corresponds to **orange**.
[4 marks for the correct answer with supporting calculation, otherwise 1 mark for rearranging the equation, 1 mark for correct substitution, 1 mark for correctly calculating the frequency of the reflected light and 1 mark for stating the colour of the light correctly]

2.2 The pigment has a rough surface, so the higher the ratio of binder to pigment, the smoother the surface *[1 mark]*. Light undergoes specular reflection from smooth surfaces, and diffuse reflection from rough surfaces *[1 mark]*. Light undergoes more specular reflection from glossy surfaces than matte surfaces, so there must be a higher ratio of binder to pigment in glossy paints than in matte paints *[1 mark]*.

3.1 E.g. Gamma radiation has hazardous effects on the human body, so using it in communications would be dangerous *[1 mark]*.

3.2 The radio wave received creates an alternating current with the same frequency as the radio wave. As current is directly proportional to potential difference, the frequency of the potential difference is equal to the frequency of the radio wave.
Each square width is equal to 2×10^{-6} s.
There are 10 squares spanning the width of the trace, so the time over which the trace spans is:
$10 \times (2 \times 10^{-6}) = 20 \times 10^{-6}$ s
1.5 wavelengths are displayed on the trace, so the period of the wave is:
$(20 \times 10^{-6}) \div 1.5 = 1.33... \times 10^{-5}$ s
$T = 1 \div f$
Rearrange for f:
$f = 1 \div T = 1 \div (1.33... \times 10^{-5}) = $ **7.5×10^4 Hz**
[4 marks for the correct answer, otherwise 1 mark for calculating the period of the wave, 1 mark for correct rearrangement and 1 mark for correct substitution.]

3.3 Radio waves are used frequently in communications, so there may be a lot of other radio waves present *[1 mark]*.

Page 47: Radiation and Temperature

1.1 20% of the energy is absorbed by the atmosphere and 10% of the energy is reflected by the atmosphere, so $100 - 20 - 10 = 70\%$ (or 0.7) is transmitted through.
Energy of radiation that is transmitted through the atmosphere $= 0.7 \times 400 = 280$ J
The ratio of energy absorbed by the planet's surface to the energy reflected by the planet's surface is 5:2.
So the radiation that passes through the atmosphere transfers $\frac{5}{7}$ of its energy to the surface.
Energy absorbed by the surface $= \frac{5}{7} \times 280 = $ **200 J**
[2 marks for the correct answer, otherwise 1 mark for correctly calculating the energy of the radiation that is transmitted through the atmosphere]

1.2 The temperature of the surface of the planet will decrease *[1 mark]* because the moon will block radiation from the star from reaching the planet and transferring energy to the surface *[1 mark]*.

Pages 48-49: Exploring Structures Using Waves

1.1 How to grade your answer:
Level 0:   There is no relevant information. *[No marks]*
Level 1:   A brief explanation of the properties of S-waves and P-waves is given, but no clear link is made to how these properties demonstrate that the Earth has layers. *[1 to 2 marks]*
Level 2:   A well-written, detailed and coherent explanation is given. The relevant properties of both kinds of seismic wave are stated. These properties are clearly linked to a detailed explanation of how we know the Earth contains layers, with reference to the 'shadow zones' in Figure 1. *[3 to 4 marks]*
Here are some points your answer may include:
P-waves can travel through liquids and solids.
S-waves can travel through solids, but not liquids.
S-waves are detected near to point X, so they are able to travel through the outer layer of the Earth.

This means that the outer layer of the Earth must be solid.
There are 'shadow zones' on the opposite side of the Earth
where P-waves are detected but S-waves are not.
Since P-waves are able to pass through the centre of the Earth
but S-waves are not, there must be liquid present.
So the Earth must have a liquid core surrounded by a solid
outer layer.

1.2   The wave slows down as it passes from the mantle to the
outer core, so it refracts and bends towards the normal to the
boundary *[1 mark]*. The wave speeds up as it passes back
from the outer core to the mantle, so it refracts and bends
away from the normal to the boundary *[1 mark]*.

2   How to grade your answer:
    Level 0:   There is no relevant information. *[No marks]*
    Level 1:   There is a brief explanation of how ultrasound
         can be used to distinguish real gold from fake
         gold with a tungsten core. The reflection
         of ultrasound when it reaches a boundary is
         mentioned. *[1 to 2 marks]*
    Level 2:   There is a clear and detailed explanation of how
         the partial reflection or speed of ultrasound
         can be used to distinguish real gold from fake
         gold with a tungsten core. A description of the
         detected differences between the two bars is
         given. *[3 to 4 marks]*
    Here are some points your answer may include:
    Ultrasound is partially reflected when it crosses the boundary
between two different materials.
In a solid gold bar, the first reflection would occur when
ultrasound enters the bar.
Then there would be a second reflection when the ultrasound
hits/reaches the other side of the bar.
So if the bar was solid gold there would be two reflections
in total.
If the bar has a tungsten core, there would be a third
reflection when the ultrasound enters the tungsten.
There would also be a fourth reflection when the ultrasound
leaves the tungsten.
So if the bar had a tungsten core then there would be four
reflections.
The speed of a sound wave will be different in gold than it is
in tungsten.
Measure the width of the bar and the time it takes for an
ultrasound signal to travel through the bar.
From this the speed of the ultrasound wave can be calculated.
Compare the speed measured to the speed of ultrasound in
gold — if it is different, the bar is fake.

3   The distance the ultrasound travels at the deepest point is
twice the depth, because it travels from the ship to the sea
floor, and from the sea floor back up to the ship:
$175 \times 2 = 350$ m
The speed of the ultrasound wave:
$s = vt$ so $v = s \div t$
         $= 350 \div 0.23 = 1521.7...$ m/s
The distance the ultrasound travels at the second point is
twice the depth like before:
$63 \times 2 = 126$ m
The time taken for the wave to travel to the sea floor and
back at the second point:
$s = vt$ so $t = s \div v$
         $= 126 \div 1521.7...$
         $= 0.0828 = \textbf{0.83 s (to 2 s.f.)}$
*[5 marks for the correct answer, otherwise 1 mark for
correct substitution into v = s ÷ t, 1 mark for correctly
calculating the speed of ultrasound in sea water,
1 mark for correct substitution into t = s ÷ v and 1 mark for
the correct unrounded answer]*

Topic 7 — Magnetism and Electromagnetism

Pages 50-51: Magnetism and Electromagnetism

1.1   How to grade your answer:
    Level 0:   There is no relevant information. *[No marks]*
    Level 1:   There is a basic explanation of how a current
         in the wire causes the motion of the coil in the
         field. *[1 to 2 marks]*
    Level 2:   There is a good explanation of how a current
         in the wire causes the motion of the coil and
         an explanation of what happens if the current
         is either removed, increased or reversed (or
         basic descriptions of at least two of the three).
         [3 to 4 marks]
    Level 3:   There is a detailed explanation of how a current
         in the wire causes the motion of the coil and the
         forces involved. There is an explanation of what
         happens if the current is removed, increased and
         reversed. *[5 to 6 marks]*
    Here are some points your answer may include:
Current from the circuit flows round the coil.
This produces a magnetic field around the coil.
This magnetic field interacts with the magnetic field of the
magnets.
The parts of the coil perpendicular to the field, i.e. the sides
of the coil, feel a force due to the motor effect.
The forces on the two sides act in opposite directions which
causes rotation.
The coil (and so the pointer) rotates and the spring stretches
(or compresses).
As the spring stretches (or compresses) it applies a force to
the coil in the opposite direction to the force from the motor
effect.
The force applied by the spring increases as the coil rotates
more.
The forces will eventually balance and the pointer will come
to a rest.
The larger the current through the coil, the larger the force
due to the motor effect, and the more the pointer will turn
before the forces balance.
When the current stops flowing, the force disappears and the
spring returns the pointer back to its original position.
If the current is reversed then the pointer moves in the
opposite direction because the force on each side of the coil
is reversed (Fleming's left-hand rule).

1.2   The magnetic field produced by the curved magnets is always
perpendicular to the plane of the core as it rotates, so the
force on the coil is constant *[1 mark]*. This allows the scale
to be linear *[1 mark]*.

1.3   E.g.

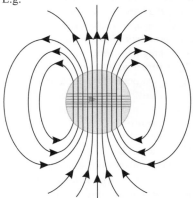

*[1 mark for correct shaped field lines that are parallel and
equally spaced inside the coil and curved outside, 1 mark
for the correct direction marked on the magnetic field lines]*

1.4
$$F = 10 \text{ mN} = 10 \div 1000 = 0.01 \text{ N}$$
$$l = 25 \text{ mm} = 25 \div 1000 = 0.025 \text{ m}$$
$$F = BIl \text{ so } B = F \div Il$$
$$= \frac{0.01}{2 \times 0.025} = \mathbf{0.2 \text{ T}}$$

[4 marks for correct answer with units, otherwise 1 mark for correct rearrangement, 1 mark for correct substitution and 1 mark for correct unit or correct value]

1.5 E.g. pass known currents through the galvanometer and mark them on the scale where the pointer comes to a rest *[1 mark]*.

1.6 Any two from: e.g. decrease the strength of the magnets/ magnetic field *[1 mark]*. / Decrease the length of the iron core/side of coil perpendicular to the field *[1 mark]*. / Decrease the number of turns on the coil *[1 mark]*.

The overall force needs to be smaller so that the pointer doesn't move as far for the same current. F = BIl for each wire in the side of the coil, so to decrease the force, the strength of the magnetic field, the length or the number of wires need to be decreased. You could also have suggested using a stiffer spring, so that the force due to the motor effect and the force due to the spring become balanced at a much smaller extension.

Pages 52-54: The Generator Effect and Transformers

1.1 High potential difference and low current *[1 mark]*.
To be effective, the national grid needs to transmit a large amount of power *[1 mark]*.
$P = IV$ so I or V needs to be high *[1 mark]*.
To be efficient, the national grid needs to minimise energy losses. A high current leads to energy losses as the wires heat up and transfer energy to the thermal energy store of the surroundings, so the electricity need to be transmitted at a low current *[1 mark]*.

1.2 $1.2 \text{ kA} = 1.2 \times 1000 = 1200 \text{ A}$
Using $\frac{V_p}{V_s} = \frac{n_p}{n_s}$ and $I_p V_p = I_s V_s$
$$I_s = \frac{I_p V_p}{V_s} = I_p \times \frac{n_p}{n_s}$$
$$= 1200 \times \frac{60\,000}{45\,000} = \mathbf{1600 \text{ A}} \text{ (= } 1.6 \times 10^3 \text{ A)}$$

[3 marks for correct answer, otherwise 1 mark for getting an expression involving current and number of turns and 1 mark for correct substitution]

1.3 Any one from: e.g. Assume 100% efficiency / no energy losses / no energy transferred to the thermal energy stores of the surroundings *[1 mark]*.

1.4 Direct current only flows in one direction *[1 mark]*. If there is no change in current, there is no changing magnetic field *[1 mark]* so there is no induction of potential difference in the secondary coil *[1 mark]*.

2.1 How to grade your answer:
Level 0:   There is no relevant information. *[No marks]*
Level 1:   There is a brief explanation of how a generator works. *[1 to 2 marks]*
Level 2:   There is a good explanation of how a generator works and which type of current each generator produces has been identified (ac or dc). *[3 to 4 marks]*
Level 3:   There is a detailed explanation of how a generator works and an explanation of how the different generators produce ac and dc. *[5 to 6 marks]*

Here are some points your answer may include:
As the coil turns, the magnetic field through it changes.
This causes a potential difference to be induced across the ends of the coil.
If the wire is part of a complete circuit, current flows through the coil.
An alternator has slip rings which allow the ends of the rotating coil to stay connected to the same ends of the circuit at all times.

As the coil turns, the direction of the current induced changes direction as the direction of motion on each arm reverses every half turn.
The current produced is alternating (ac).
The dynamo has a split ring which swaps the connection between the rotating coil and the rest of the circuit every half turn, keeping the current flowing in one direction.
The current produced is direct (dc).

2.2 A is the alternator output current because the current changes direction every half turn *[1 mark]*.

2.3 Period of alternator, $T = 80 \text{ ms} = 80 \div 1000 = 0.08 \text{ s}$
Frequency of alternator, $f = 1 \div T$
$$= 1 \div 0.08 = \mathbf{12.5 \text{ Hz}}$$

[2 marks for the correct answer, otherwise 1 mark for correctly reading the period from the graph]

2.4 Stronger magnetic field / more turns in the coil *[1 mark]*.

Do not accept spin faster. This would also increase the frequency but you can see from the graph that the frequencies match.

3.1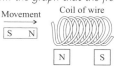

[1 mark]

The coil opposes the movement of the magnet. If you push the N pole into the coil then the coil tries to do the opposite by pushing the N pole back out.

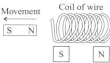

[1 mark]

The coil opposes the movement of the magnet. If you pull the N pole away from the coil then the coil tries to do the opposite by pulling the N pole back in.

3.2 The coil of wire should be put into a magnetic field that is perpendicular to the wire at all times/a radial magnetic field/a magnetic field caused by one pole inside the coil and one pole around it *[1 mark]*. Sound waves hitting the cone cause it to vibrate *[1 mark]*. This causes the coil of wire to vibrate back and forth inside the magnetic field of the permanent magnet *[1 mark]* which induces a current in the coil of wire due to the generator effect *[1 mark]*.

Topic 8 — Space Physics

Pages 55-57: Red-Shift and Orbits

1.1 The universe is expanding, and so galaxy X is moving away from the Earth *[1 mark]*. Red-shift occurs when an object that is emitting light is moving away from the observer, and so the wavelengths of the light from galaxy X are stretched out and the light is red-shifted *[1 mark]*.

1.2 Read wavelengths of equivalent dark lines from the spectra and find difference between them:
E.g. reading fourth dark line:
Wavelength in spectrum B, $\lambda = 656 \text{ nm}$
Wavelength in spectrum A = 670 nm
So, $\Delta\lambda = 670 - 656 = 14 \text{ nm}$
$$z = \frac{\Delta\lambda}{\lambda} = \frac{14}{656} = 0.021341... = \mathbf{0.021} \text{ (to 2 s.f.)}$$
(Accept between 0.019 and 0.023)
[4 marks for correct answer, otherwise 1 mark for reading correct pair of values from the spectra, 1 mark for correct substitution and 1 mark for correct unrounded answer]

1.3 Galaxy Y is further from Earth, and so the light emitted from it will undergo a larger red-shift *[1 mark]*. The range of wavelengths in which the absorption lines sit has been increased so much that these lines are no longer in the visible spectrum *[1 mark]*. The astronomer could observe the infrared radiation reaching Earth from galaxy Y (as the absorption lines will have been shifted into the infrared part of the electromagnetic spectrum) *[1 mark]*.

2.1 The planet's speed is constant, but its direction is constantly changing, so its velocity is changing *[1 mark]*. Since acceleration is the change in velocity over time, it is constantly accelerating *[1 mark]*.

2.2 E.g.

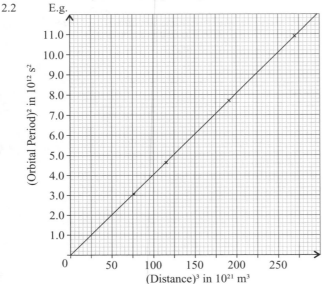

[1 mark for correctly plotting the point, 1 mark for suitable straight line of best fit]

2.3 Comparing Kepler's third law, $T^2 = kr^3$, to the equation of a straight line, $y = mx + c$.
$y = T^2$, $m = k$, $x = r^3$ and $c = 0$
So Kepler's constant, k = gradient of the graph, m
E.g. $k = \dfrac{\text{change in } y}{\text{change in } x} = \dfrac{10.1 \times 10^{12} - 0}{250 \times 10^{21} - 0} = $ **4.04×10^{-11} s²/m³**
(Accept between 4.00×10^{-11} s²/m³ and 4.08×10^{-11} s²/m³)
[2 marks for correct answer, otherwise 1 mark for attempt to calculate gradient]

2.4 Charon's orbital speed will have decreased when it moved to its current orbit from its old orbit *[1 mark]*, because, as the moon is further from Pluto, it experiences a weaker gravitational force towards Pluto, and so it must travel slower in order to remain in a stable orbit *[1 mark]*.

Mixed Questions for Paper 2

Pages 58-62: Mixed Questions for Paper 2

1.1 Before the collision, the momentum of the club is:
$p = mv = 0.40 \times 20 = 8$ kg m/s
The ball isn't moving, so it has a momentum of 0 kg m/s.
So the total momentum before the collision is 8 kg m/s.
After the collision, the momentum of the club is:
$p = mv = 0.40 \times 15 = 6$ kg m/s
The total momentum before the collision must be equal to the total momentum after the collision, so the ball must have a momentum of:
$8 - 6 = 2$ kg m/s
45 g = $45 \div 1000 = 0.045$ kg
$p = mv$
Rearrange the equation for v to find the size of ball's velocity:
$v = p \div m = 2 \div 0.045 = 44.4... = $ **44 m/s (to 2 s.f.)**
[5 marks for correct answer, otherwise 1 mark for correctly calculating the total momentum before the collision, 1 mark for correct rearrangement, 1 mark for correct substitution into $v = p \div m$ and 1 mark for correct unrounded answer]

1.2 The final velocity of the ball is 0 m/s, so:
$a = \dfrac{\Delta v}{t} = \dfrac{3 - 0}{5} = 0.6$ m/s²
$F = ma = 0.045 \times 0.6 = $ **0.027 N**
[4 marks for correct answer, otherwise 1 mark for correct substitution into $a = \dfrac{\Delta v}{t}$, 1 mark for calculating the acceleration correctly and 1 mark for correct substitution into $F = ma$]

1.3 $F = \dfrac{m\Delta v}{\Delta t}$, so the change in velocity of the ball is directly proportional to the contact time *[1 mark]*. Since the force and golf ball mass are the same, the velocity of the second ball after it is hit will be greater due to its increased contact time *[1 mark]*.

2.1 Reading from the graph, the peak wavelength of star X is approximately 0.95 µm.
0.95 µm = 0.95×10^{-6} m
$\lambda_{peak}T = 2.9 \times 10^{-3}$
Rearrange for T:
$T = (2.9 \times 10^{-3}) \div \lambda_{peak}$
$= (2.9 \times 10^{-3}) \div (0.95 \times 10^{-6}) = 3052.6...$ K
Convert the temperature to °C:
$3052.6... - 273 = 2779.63... = $ **2800 °C (to 2 s.f.)**
[5 marks for the correct answer, otherwise 1 mark for reading the peak wavelength from the graph correctly, 1 mark for correct substitution into $T = 2.9 \times 10^{-3} \div \lambda_{peak}$, 1 mark for correctly calculating the temperature of star X in kelvin and 1 mark for correct unrounded answer]

2.2 E.g. light from star Y has been red-shifted less because it is closer to Earth, and so is moving away from Earth more slowly *[1 mark]*.

2.3 7.5 million km = $7.5 \times 10^6 \times 10^3 = 7.5 \times 10^9$ m
11.2 days = $11.2 \times 24 \times 60 \times 60 = 967\,680$ s
The distance travelled by the planet in one orbit is equal to the circumference of the orbit.
distance = $\pi \times$ diameter = $\pi \times 7.5 \times 10^9 = 2.356... \times 10^{10}$ m
Rearrange distance travelled = speed × time for speed:
speed = distance travelled ÷ time
$= (2.356... \times 10^{10}) \div 967\,680$
$= 24\,348.9014 = $ **24 000 m/s (to 2 s.f.)**
[4 marks for correct answer, otherwise 1 mark for correctly calculating the distance travelled in one orbit, 1 mark for correct substitution into speed = distance travelled ÷ time and 1 mark for correct unrounded answer]

3.1 The stone is travelling downwards *[1 mark]* with a constant acceleration *[1 mark]*.

3.2 The maximum height is reached when the stone's velocity reaches 0 m/s for the first time, which is 0.11 s after it hits the water. The distance travelled during this time is equal to the area under the graph up to this time.
Area of a triangle is 0.5 × base × height
So maximum height of the stone = 0.5 × 0.11 × 1.0
= **0.055 m**
[2 marks for the correct answer, otherwise 1 mark for reading the correct values from the graph]

3.3

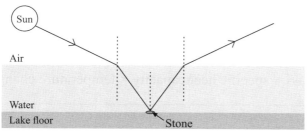

[1 mark for drawing light rays so that the angle of incidence on the stone is equal to the angle of reflection and 1 mark for drawing the light refracting away from the normal as it leaves the water]

4.1 How to grade your answer:
Level 0: There is no relevant information. *[No marks]*
Level 1: There is a basic explanation of how pressing the button results in contact between the brake plate and the rail. The production of a magnetic field is mentioned, but the mechanism by which it is produced is unclear. *[1 to 2 marks]*
Level 2: There is a well-written and detailed explanation of how pressing the button results in the production of a magnetic field in the brake plate. This is clearly linked to the production of a frictional force that causes the train to decelerate and come to a stop. *[3 to 4 marks]*
Here are some points your answer may include:
When the button is pressed, the switch closes and the circuit is complete.
The ac power supply provides a current through the coil of wire.
This causes a magnetic field to be created around the coil.
The steel brake plate is inside the coil's magnetic field, so it becomes an induced magnet.
The brake plate is attracted to the steel rail and moves downwards so that it is in contact with the rail.
Friction between the brake plate and the rail acts in the opposite direction to the train's velocity.
This resultant force causes the train to decelerate until it comes to a stop.

4.2 0.4 MN $= 0.4 × 10^6 = 400\ 000$ N
$F = ma$
Rearrange for a to find the deceleration of the train:
$a = F ÷ m = 400\ 000 ÷ 200\ 000 = 2$ m/s^2
Deceleration is negative acceleration, so:
$a = -2$ m/s^2
$v^2 - u^2 = 2as$
Rearrange for s:
$s = \dfrac{v^2 - u^2}{2a} = \dfrac{0^2 - 28^2}{2 × (-2)} = \mathbf{196\ m}$
[5 marks for correct answer, otherwise 1 mark for correct substitution into $a = F ÷ m$, 1 mark for correctly calculating the deceleration, 1 mark for rearranging $v^2 - u^2 = 2as$ for s and 1 mark for correct substitution into $s = \dfrac{v^2 - u^2}{2a}$]

Alternatively you could calculate the energy in the train's kinetic energy store using $KE = \frac{1}{2}mv^2$. Then rearrange the work done equation, $W = Fd$, to find the distance travelled.

5.1 White light contains all colours, but the red filter only allows red light to pass through, so it appears red *[1 mark]*. The helmet absorbs red light/all colours apart from blue, so it does not reflect any red light and so appears black *[1 mark]*.

5.2 There are 8 complete waves in the diagram and it spans 5.0 seconds.
Frequency is equal to the number of waves in one second, so the average frequency = $8 ÷ 5.0 = 1.6$ Hz
$v = f × λ$
Rearrange for $λ$:
$λ = v ÷ f$
$= 6400 ÷ 1.6$
$= \mathbf{4000\ m}$
[4 marks for the correct answer, otherwise 1 mark for correctly calculating the frequency, 1 mark for correctly rearranging wave speed equation and 1 mark for correct substitution into the wave speed equation]

5.3 Seismic waves are detected at the station before the person hears the explosion. *[1 mark]*
Sound travels at approximately 330 m/s in air.
2.1 km = 2.1 × 1000 = 2100 m.
Rearrange speed = distance ÷ time for time to find the time taken for the sound waves to arrive. time = distance ÷ speed = 2100 ÷ 330 = 6.36... s.
So the seismic waves are detected at the station first.

Equations List

Here are some equations you might find useful when you're working through the book —
you'll be given these equations in the exams.

Topic 1 — Energy

$E_e = \frac{1}{2}ke^2$	elastic potential energy $= 0.5 \times$ spring constant $\times$ (extension)^2
$\Delta E = mc\Delta\theta$	change in thermal energy $=$ mass $\times$ specific heat capacity $\times$ temperature change

Topic 3 — Particle Model of Matter

$E = mL$	thermal energy for a change of state $=$ mass $\times$ specific latent heat
$pV = $ constant	pressure $\times$ volume $=$ constant (for gases)

Topic 5 — Forces

$p = h\rho g$	pressure due to a column of liquid $=$ height of column $\times$ density of liquid $\times$ gravitational field strength (g)
$v^2 - u^2 = 2as$	(final velocity)^2 $-$ (initial velocity)^2 $= 2 \times$ acceleration $\times$ distance
$F = \dfrac{m\Delta v}{\Delta t}$	force $= \dfrac{\text{change in momentum}}{\text{time taken}}$

Topic 6 — Waves

period $= \dfrac{1}{\text{frequency}}$
magnification $= \dfrac{\text{image height}}{\text{object height}}$

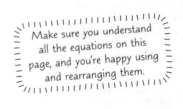

Make sure you understand all the equations on this page, and you're happy using and rearranging them.

Topic 7 — Magnetism and Electromagnetism

$F = BIl$	force on a current-carrying conductor (at right-angles to a magnetic field) $=$ magnetic flux density $\times$ current $\times$ length
$\dfrac{V_p}{V_s} = \dfrac{n_p}{n_s}$	$\dfrac{\text{potential difference across primary coil}}{\text{potential difference across secondary coil}} = \dfrac{\text{number of turns in primary coil}}{\text{number of turns in secondary coil}}$
$V_sI_s = V_pI_p$	potential difference across primary coil $\times$ current in primary coil $=$ potential difference across secondary coil $\times$ current in secondary coil

PA9Q41